BLA[CK]
PUBLISHING

FAIRY TALES

WHEN ARCHITECTURE

TELLS A STORY

This edition first published 2014
© **Copyright 2014 Blank Space**

ISBN 978-0-9903664-0-9

Books are available at quantity discounts when used to promote product or services. For information please write to the Blank Space marketing division at **office@blankspaceproject.com.**

Visit online at **www.blankspaceproject.com**

Printed and bound in the United States of America.

INTRODUCTION

O nce upon a time, we challenged architects to tell us stories, and design them too. The book you are holding is the result of that challenge, a collection of entries to "Fairy Tales," the world's first architectural storytelling competition, organized by Blank Space in 2013-14.

We created "Fairy Tales" because we recognized a split between architecture and the rest of the world by observing how architects only talk to each other. To make architecture more accessible, we challenged architects to break out of their niche and come up with new ways to engage the public. So we asked them to write a story.

Fairy tales might seem like a foreign topic for the architecture community – but at their core is the power of communication. Fairy tales are relatable, yet sophisticated and nuanced, just like great architecture. As children, fairy tales are our gateway to significance, and to making sense of the intricacies of the real world. They present us with problems and the ways in which they are dealt with by their protagonists. They are paradigmatic of experiences we haven't yet had, decisions we haven't yet made, and feelings we haven't yet felt. Without us being cognizant, they are our first training in logic, empathy, and creativity.

Communication is at the core of design. When architects forget that, they produce dull architecture. There is a type of dull architecture that is simply uninspired: it embodies its function, referentially, and doesn't say more. There is a second type that is more deceitful. It hides its lack of soul in shiny, vacuous renderings. It tells a false story of happiness, togetherness and good life, but it doesn't fulfill its promises. It only rings with the sound of the millions of dollars funneled into its development.

The business of architecture relies on the mass production of these types of projects, sacrificing architecture's true spirit and potential. Marginalized in its role as an aesthetic commodity, trapped in technical jargon, architecture has lost its ability to send universal messages. Architecture no longer represents culture in its time, and it has failed to address issues at the core of human existence.

We call this a 'curse' cast on architecture by an evil witch: Banality. Architecture competitions are also affected by this curse. Even though they should be the place for architects to unleash their imagination, most competitions mimic scenarios that are those of the architectural trade, and give the entrants requirements and constraints that leave very little room for true invention.

We set out to break this spell by challenging creatives to abandon their comfort zone altogether. We gave no indications of typology, scope, location, or budget. No constraints or requirements besides one: write an architecture fairy tale, and design it too. The response was truly astonishing.

Over 300 teams from 50 countries around the world participated in the first iteration of the Fairy

Tales competition. The astonishing diversity and quality of the entries is a testament to the importance of pushing architects beyond the known boundaries of their trade, and picking their brains in unexpected and unconventional ways.

In the words of the distinguished juror, Professor Jack Zipes, "the most important takeaway from the competition is that architects, designers and creatives from all over the world, while bringing their unique perspective to the challenge, also share some fundamental enthusiasms and preoccupations. Expressing these feelings in the form of a fairy tale, these creatives took it upon themselves to initiate a more inclusive conversation on architecture, which is up to all of us to keep developing."

In the following pages you will find a selection of thought-provoking architectural fairy tales, including the winning entries and honorable mentions awarded by the jury. The entries seamlessly blend into an unexpected polyphony of architectural messages, giving new strength to architecture as a force of social innovation and dialogue. If there's a moral to these architectural fairy tales, it is that architecture is an untapped source of magnificent stories waiting to be imagined, visualized and built. The world can't wait to be told stories like this. Let's write more of them.

Happily ever after,
Matthew Hoffman and Francesca Giuliani-Hoffman,
Founders of Blank Space

Contents

Third
Place Prize
Winner

OSCAR UPON A TIME

By Joseph Altshuler, Mary Altshuler & Zachary Morrison

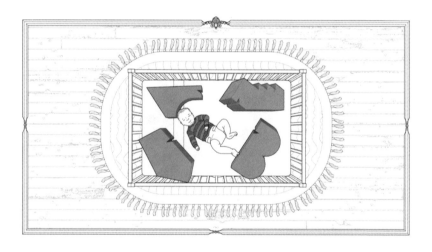

On the eve of the day that marked four months since Oscar's birth, four objects were placed upon him. Mother's hand lay firmly on his abdomen and held him still. Father's breath warmed each of his palms and then both of his soles. Grandmother circled him four times while humming an unrecognizable melody. Rough came first. Father wrapped Oscar's right hand around its edges and moved it back and forth. Rough chuckled as Oscar scratched each groove. Next came Slick. Father cupped Oscar's left hand around Slick and held it there so that it wouldn't slip away, and for now Slick kept still. Third was Firm. Father lifted Oscar into the air and placed Oscar's right foot on Firm. He tilted the baby just so, and Oscar felt his weight rest on the object. Firm tensed. Last was Sponge. Father held Oscar in one hand, face down, until he gurgled and drooled. Sponge sucked in each drop of saliva and swelled. Then, Father handed Oscar to Grandmother, who continued humming until he slept soundly. She rested Oscar in his crib, and she situated Rough,

Slick, Firm, and Sponge in the four corners around
him. Each of them breathed and dreamt.

They woke up closer on the morning of Oscar's
eighth birthday. He stood on his toes and put
his ear against the vent. He could tell that his
parents were still sleeping. That he had woken
up before them was typical, and as of late they
had announced that he was too old to join them
in bed. "Just play quietly until we're up," they
had told him yesterday. But Oscar didn't want
to play, he wanted to be held. He shifted from
bed to floor, and he sat with his knees bent and
his arms wrapped around his head. "Lean back,"
offered Firm, as he stood tall behind Oscar.
And so Oscar leaned. "Push here," suggested
Rough, as he edged his way forward. Oscar let
out a primal yawn as he gripped his toes around
Rough and pushed back hard. Sponge wriggled in
between and said, "Nestle." Oscar let his neck
relax in the crevice that Sponge had created for
him. Slick lingered and watched, unsure of where
he would fit. But when Oscar lifted his hips to
shift his weight, he saw his chance. He eased his
way across the floorboards to the space beneath
Oscar, thereby completing the peace. Each of
them breathed and waited.

Together, they watched the minutes and hours
pass. Oscar paced up and down the hall, and
then he sat near his door, and then he paced up
and down the hall, and then he settled into the

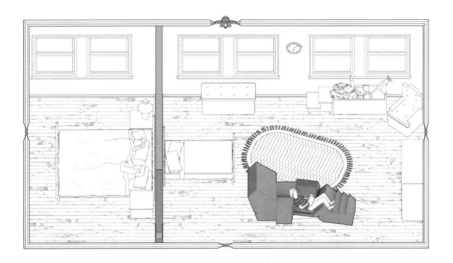

common room. "I'll be back soon," his roommate
had told him. "This party isn't going to last
forever." Oscar had lost his keys a week ago,
and relying on his roommate to get him into their
shared dorm at his desired times since then had
been treacherous. Worse now that it was only
five hours before he had to be awake for his first
class. "Dammit," Oscar muttered as he banged
his fist against the wall. He leaned back, threw
his book down, and drooped his head in defeat.
Sponge stepped forward first, and without saying
a word he formed a table in front of Oscar and
propped up his book. "You can read comfortably

now," said Sponge. "Warm your toes under me while you study." Rough took three deep breaths and then reached out to form a blockade between his friend and passersby. "Just relax," he said. "You're protected." Then Slick said, "I've got this." He clung onto Rough's edges and formed an arched rooftop that let in just a crevice of the hallway's fluorescent glow. Firm joined the others, and further enclosed the serene space. "I've left a peephole for you," he said. Oscar looked down, around, up, and out with wide eyes. "I take back my dammit," he whispered. Each of them breathed and reclined.

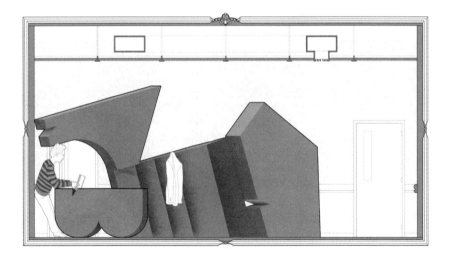

"Stand up straight," Oscar's wife nagged. "If you slouch this much at twenty-nine, you'll be a hunchback by sixty for sure. Besides, I want to see your height against the door-frames." They were making plans for their new home. Their first home. They had closed three days ago. She still wasn't convinced. "It's missing so much," she grumbled as they stepped through the front door. "Walls for one. It just needs..." she tapered off. "Character," said Oscar. "Right," she responded. They held hands and sauntered around their square footage. This time, with each turn things looked a bit different. "Look," said Oscar as he gestured toward the wall. Firm felt proud of the way in which he had become a cornerstone of their home, holding up the roof. Sponge beamed when they turned toward the ramp he now offered from the kitchen to the office. "This is less bland than I remember it," said Oscar's wife. "I saw the potential all along," Oscar mumbled. "What?" she asked. "Nothing," he said. "Let's keep going. How about upstairs?" "Upstairs?" she asked. "We don't have any stairs to speak of." "Yes we do," he said and pointed. Rough grinned as the couple stepped up onto the first stair. He knew that he had formed into a perfect combination of angle and comfort. Slick waited patiently for the couple to reach his bedroom loft. "Interesting, this really is better than I remember it," Oscar's wife said. "Everything seems to be,"

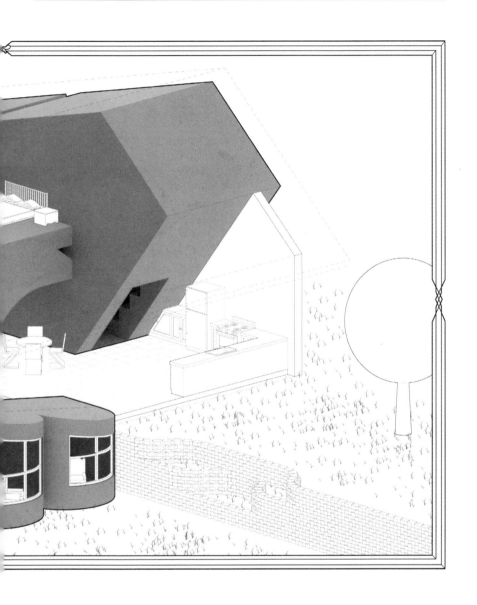

Oscar responded. "But what happened?" she asked. Each of them breathed and wondered.

Oscar asked no questions and thought no thoughts as he lay on the grass patch outside of where his home used to be. He just lay and felt his existence. By shifting his head from side to side, he managed to dig a personalized mold into the ground. The dirt mixed with his grey hair, and it cooled his neck. He extended each of his arms and grabbed fistfuls of the grass. It tickled his palms. He stretched each of his legs and went back and forth between flexing and pointing his toes. Oscar felt at peace, but he also felt empty. He thought he needed nothing, yet he was longing for something. He didn't know what it was, but the others did. "Psst," whispered Slick, and he motioned across the grass patch. Rough, Sponge, and Firm heard him and knew what to do. Though they were now stretched high upwards and low downwards, each of them still had just enough agility to inch forward until they touched one of Oscar's arms or legs. "That's enough," said Sponge. "He feels us." And Oscar did. He didn't know how it had happened, but the buildings near him seemed a bit closer now, and he felt a bit bigger. It was if they were hugging him, and in doing so they were transferring to him some of their strength. Oscar knew he wouldn't live forever, but in that moment, his existence felt one step closer to permanent.

THE SECRET LIFE OF NEW WORLD TOWERS

By Berenika Boberska

I. The Flying Dutchman

It was an overcast night for most, meaning only the tops of skyscrapers appeared through the sea of low lying clouds - like islands.

With all the aplomb of a dandy sailing in, he seemed slightly disappointed about the lack of audience: the usual dispersed crowd of somnambulists, that more receptive part of the population. His blackberry navigation system told him he was almost there - the Prince's Tower top floor champagne bar. (His was a curious mix of fine tailoring, latest gadgetry and unscrupulous bon-vivre)

The ship floated deeper into the city archipelago, steering in-between the rooftops, careful to avoid the spiky bamboo scaffoldings. The clouds below all aglow with orange and blue from the neon lights they smothered.

Suddenly the ship tilted steeply, caught like a fly in a web of illegal washing lines, which stretched

between two scruffy looking high-rises. There was
no choice but to seek refuge on one of them. What
in the darkness seemed like an un-kept topiary instead of a rooftop, turned out to be a dense forest
of trees and antennas. Standing at the edge of it,
reluctant, he hesitated - then entered.

A forest, however small, and this one was only
the area of 4 Hong Kong apartments, always swal-
lows the visitor and subjects him to its own whims.

Upon closer inspection there was an order in
this thicket of nature and technology, like a well-
loved garden, but with enough lapses of attention
to allow for idiosyncrasy. For example, a satellite
dish served as an orchid bed, a tangle of bird nests
and ribbons stifled an antenna. It made him think
that the caretaker of this garden must surely be a
woman. Or perhaps it was his hidden wish.

There were other things. On the second night
he came across a clearing which looked like a tiny
office amongst the trees. A desk, a computer, two
lamps, notes and drawings clipped to branches all
around. The notion that he wasn't alone on this
rooftop didn't calm him, but filled him with fear. He
begun to suspect that the other person knew his
whereabouts at all times and purposefully avoided
him, leaving pots of tea and food for him to find.
With a sinking heart he saw his once fear-inspiring
ship gradually transform into a hanging garden of
lichens and aerial plants. The upper strata of the
city seemed to have the climate of a cloud-forest –
the ancient timber of the ship was no match for the
humidity, heat, and the all-consuming tropical flora.

The Flying Dutchman was captured.

II. The Mechanical Floor

A woman whose lover only visits her at night becomes suspicious.

She lives on the 48th floor of a residential high-rise in the New Territories.

One night, she attaches a red thread to his toe whilst he is asleep. Just before dawn he leaves, but this time she is able to follow him. The thread leads out into the corridor and then to the stairwell. No-one usually goes there, especially on the upper floors.

The stairwell is humid and warm; the walls seem furry with mildew. She treads carefully in-between the fragile fungus blooms on the stairs, it's like trying to separate warm kittens with your hand. The red thread leads on up several flights of stairs towards the mechanical floor.

And there, behind metal doors, in a cavernous space of humming machinery and ductwork, amongst filigree ruffled dresses of mushrooms festooning every surface, cascading in layered garlands from the pipework above - there - his true identity is revealed. He is the King Elf, unable to find a clearing in the forest of high-rises, forced to retreat into the interior caverns. His skin seems both powdery and wet, her fingers leave slippery traces like snails.

She will stay there now, making a garden out of the more colorful of poisonous fungi, a sort of mini-golf caricature landscape of the outside world she remembers still.

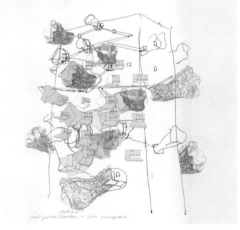

III. The Louis Vuitton Penthouse Fires

The New World Towers have always been a mix of real and unreal estate.

This was the cause of countless disputes, especially when it came to determining the saleable value of the apartments. In fact a whole shadow industry had sprung up which busied itself with the seemingly simple task of floor area calculations.

The companies conducted surveys, often very dangerous, of the "unreal" property extensions.

Most structures had little usable area, but the voluminous and eccentric "space-grabbing" contraptions had a profound effect on the perceived size of the apartments, which, as one New World Tower resident put it, are always too small (Jerry Yao, Sham Shui Po, Happy View Terrace).

Over time a conversion system emerged between the real and the unreal estate, which made things a little easier.

New World Towers begun to "blossom" with now quasi-illegal balcony extensions: bamboo structures clad with brightly printed paper and festooned with lampoons, garlands, washing lines, satellite dishes, bird cages, external storage baskets full of anything from vegetables to shoes.

The origin of these structures can possibly be linked to a folklore tradition of dzi-dzat: replicating material possessions in paper, then ceremoniously burning the effigies to ensure comfort of the spirit in after-life. The meticulously constructed paper models range from the banal to the luxurious: microwaves, cutlery, Prada shoes, clothes, credit cards and cup-cakes.

Soon enough this tradition was adapted to express the lavish cornucopia of desires of the living - for ever larger scale luxury goods: jacuzzis, cars and penthouses were constructed out of paper at 1:1 scale, and then set on fire.

This is exactly what happened one day. A quick fire traveled the height of a 50-storey high-rise in the New Territories and consumed all the paper balcony extensions in one giant puff.

This became known as the Louis Vuitton Penthouse Fires.

IV. Façade Ruffles

- a Cautionary Tale

"Feral structures and actions,
hairy buildings, thickets, ruffles and fur -
growing suddenly
and in inappropriate places,
like overflowing bubble baths -
these small things
begin radical transformations of
even the most rational of spaces
it begins with a love story......"

This is a story about a woman who lives in one of the generic residential tower blocks in the New Territories – its façade indistinguishable from any other.

She is secretly in love with her neighbor from the apartment below.

When she leans out of her window – she can just about see his windowsill and sometimes, she can catch a glimpse of him.

She tries to attract his attention by hanging a frilly item of laundry to dry outside her window, on one of the expandable washing-line contraptions.

When that fails to do the trick, she hangs a huge ruffled dress; it billows out in the upward draft like a giant bell-jar.

When he still does not notice she begins to construct and embellish a dress that is larger still – adding more ruffles to it every day until it becomes a space.

The neighbors begin to talk: but she refuses to take it down. She cannot anyway; it is now welded to a metal guardrail of her balcony and tied back to the façade by a spider web of tension cables.

She lounges around in her structure all day, beside the 27th floor.

She completely forgets about the neighbor.

Over time, other structures begin to appear. This blossoming of the façade creates a new shared space. The high-rise itself becomes forgotten, like a spell-bound structure overgrown by an engulfing thicket. It is now hidden from view and free to transform.

ENDEAVOURISM

By Mark Rukamathu & Yarinda Bunnag

E ndeavourism believes in Universe. 'Universe' is a practice based belief: the search for universal truths, corresponding to the exploration of outer space, set within core principles of science.

Universe was founded December 7th, 1972, coinciding with 'The Blue Marble,' a photograph of the Earth taken by the crew of Apollo 17. This was not the first time we humans had observed the Earth in its entirety. However, it was the first time such a vivid image of the Earth was seen, as a fragile object belonging to the larger universe, fostering

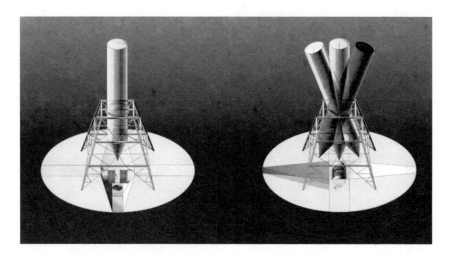

an awareness of our home planet. This realization marked a shift in our comprehension of the cosmos and rendered traditional unscientific beliefs primitive.

Adherents of Endeavourism are known as 'Endeavourists.' The name Endeavourism is based on the decommissioned space shuttle orbiter, Endeavour (now housed within the House of Endeavour). Endeavour symbolizes the triumphal human spirit: propelling ourselves forward via science and technology.

Endeavourism teaches that science is the means for understanding the universe, and technology is the vehicle to achieve our goals. Endeavourists believe in the Trinity of space shuttle Endeavour: the Nose, the Body and the Boosters. The Nose being the first organ to penetrate the atmosphere into outer space. The Body being the container of knowledge and the search for universal truth. The Boosters propel one forward and allow for discoveries. These three parts are distinct yet coexist in unity. The Trinity is the foundation of Endeavourist faith.

The House of Endeavour sits atop a parking garage 6 miles south of downtown Los Angeles. It consists of 25 great towers: a radio tower, periscopes with rotating heads, wind organs of ranging sounds, chimney stacks with exhaust fans, and telescopes with spinning lenses. The garage is surrounded by a concrete moat of cars with seven bridges stretching across. As you transverse the bridge, you observe an army of vehicles below and a forest of towers ahead.

The great towers surround the body of Endeavour. The orbiter sits partially entombed in the garage at the center of the fortress, shrouded in protective scaffolding of spiral walkways.

Endeavourists gather at every solstice and equinox. Devotees voyage from near and far to attend the assembly. Most drive and park their cars directly below the House.

Of the 25 towers, the radio tower is the tallest. Its metal frame holds one hundred satellite dishes and signal masts, receiving cosmic frequencies from outer space including that from the International Space Station. The tower rebroadcasts signals to an FM channel that people in LA tune in and listen to the sounds from the greater expanse.

Assemblies begin promptly at 8:56 am, the time of Endeavour's final ascension. When entering the House from the northernmost bridge, the Endeavourist is welcomed by a swinging tower. The clock tower oscillates like a metronome. Inside it contains blue liquid oxygen, the same substance used to propel Endeavour into space. On the 56th minute of every hour, the tower stops vertically and releases sixteen ounces of liquid oxygen toward the magnets below. Oxygen is paramagnetic so the electromagnets attract the droplet causing it to levitate within the space between the two poles. The oxygen forms a blue orb. They call this "The Blue Marble". The Endeavourist walks down the ramp to observe the Blue Marble from below. There is a fan at the base of the tower that sucks the fumes of the evaporated oxygen downwards, forming a white curtain through which he has to pass.

Entering the shadowy nave, he sees rows of

towers peek out from the darkness. Trusses and metal frames, like tree branches in a thick forest, block out all sunlight. The only light he sees comes from glowing circular craters on the floor of the nave. At the bottom of the craters, there are altars displaying machine relics and samples of elements from outer space: Mars rovers, moon rocks, meteorites. People congregate around the craters as the faithful demonstrate their latest inventions. After the completion of each experiment, a scientist pulls on a chord and a sonorous drone fills the hall. Inverted organ towers, shaped like up-side-down flue pipes, catch the wind and transmit sounds through the nave. Different size towers create choral music of the Earth's atmosphere.

When you observe the area underneath another tower, you see an image of a city. These towers are periscopes: they show skylines and suburbs, high-rises in downtown LA and the coastline of Santa Monica. As you rotate the handle, the periscope turns and the image changes. The city always transforms and the projected images are never the same.

The Endeavourist struggles to find the shuttle within the dark mechanical forest. He walks down the nave, and suddenly the floor stops. A deep gorge ahead extends down into darkness. On the other side of this narrow drop, a black wall. The Endeavourist notices black tiles and white serial numbers across a surface. He looks up at the towering figure and recognizes it immediately. Endeavour. The distance between him and the orbiter is just beyond arm's reach. The white shuttle turns its back on the main entrance and disguises itself underneath the shadows of trusses and towers.

Underneath the nave a cylindrical void carves into the existing underground parking garage. The escalator runs parallel to the tail of Endeavour, taking the visitor down into the void.

The crypt is three stories deep. On the top two floors are two orbital chambers, each the dimension of a single parking spot. Entrance to the chamber is like going into an automatic car wash. Once inside, the chamber orbits you and your car around Endeavour. Only the bottom section of the shuttle and the boosters are visible in the crypt, suspended from the ceiling, as if they have been sliced off by the floor. The crypt is dark and damp, lit only by vehicle headlights. The headlights illuminate the boosters, floating in the center of the vault.

The base of the crypt is open. When the Endeavourist reaches the bottom he notices that it is still operating as a normal garage. There are cars parked right underneath the floating body of Endeavour. "Earthly machines coexist with the cosmic one," he whispers to himself. Columns from the existing garage remain in the void of the crypt, but the middle portions of the columns have been severed. What seems to be exposed rebar is in fact refrigerated coil tubes. Humid garage air forms ice stalactites between these broken gaps, replacing structural members with transitory ornaments.

You park your car at the bottom of the garage and get on the escalator. To your right, you see the tail's slender white and black blade tracing the slope of your ascent. The object, while worn and weathered, has an elegance and power you cannot quite grasp. As you approach the top of the escalator, a tall, blurred silhouette comes into focus. Behind layers of scaffolding shroud, Endeavour stands. You try to make out parts of the body through the dense curtain of steel members, but can only discern fragments. When you circle the figure, you notice the entrance to a set of stairs embedded within the lattice maze of steel structure.

The Endeavourist slowly climbs the helical staircase that wraps around Endeavour. Examining, he sees several platforms extending out from the main walkway towards the shuttle. These are flying "chapels" located adjacent to the key elements of Endeavour. He walks onto a chapel, each step moving closer to the shuttle. Details become monolithic. He can clearly see each tile, its identification label and every individual one across the entire orbiter's surface.

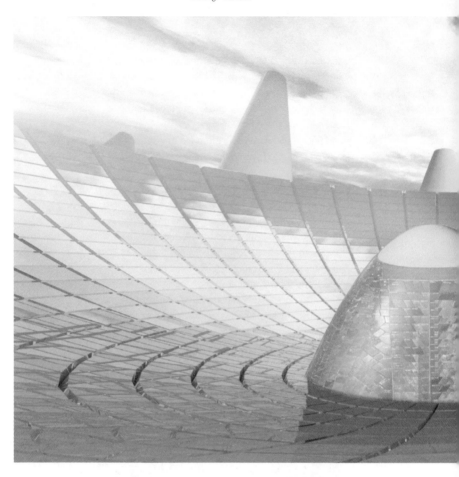

The density increases with each step. The metal
frames grow so dense it seems like a thick fog of
steel. Vertigo sets in as the fluids in his inner ears
shift erratically. He steadies himself by focusing on
Endeavour. The last chapel looks into the cockpit
windows. The astronaut seats face upwards
against the direction of gravity.

Eventually you arrive at a door. You enter. Then
there is total darkness. You keep one hand against
the wall and continue. You turn the corner. Light
floods your eyes. A bright blue rectangle.

The Endeavourist breaches the threshold and
finds himself immersed in total atmosphere.

The nose floats. A weightless black ellipsoid in

emptiness. So are you. There is nothing around you. The universe above. And that which takes you there.

The Endeavourist touches...and prays.

At dusk, the telescope towers come to life. Images of stars and galaxies animate the nave's floor. The stars rise and set, new ones appear and constellations crawl on their defined paths across the concrete surface.

Outside, people park their cars on the garage roof attending to the projection screen on the side of the House. Some have brought blankets. Seats are folded down. Families sprawled out in the beds of this year's Toyota Tundra.

THE WAY HOME

By Jonathan Russell

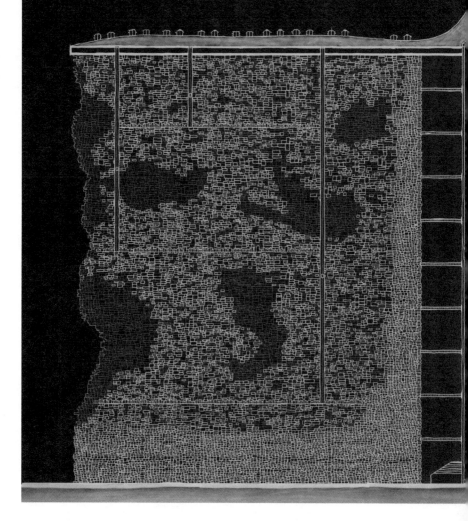

Driving back on the long, straight causeway, he peered through his windshield. Silhouetted by late evening sun the city blurred at its edges, as if he couldn't quite catch focus. There was no surface to it, no clear figure to hold - his vision grasped aimlessly at its massive, amorphous form. Closer now, he entered the city's long, trailing shadow. Its face was punctuated by lights – an uncountable matrix

reaching far into the sky, with a bright strip of
white marking the city's upper limit. Closer
again and it filled his vision – the vast, chaotic
face resolving into a near-endless field of built
form: walls and windows, balconies and ledges
in a colossal, open-weave mass of ac cumulated
humanity. Playing across faceted surfaces in the
darkening night, light spilled into clear air as the

city devoured him.

The road, its path undeviating, was quickly subsumed; he was embraced and surrounded. This was the oldest part of the laissez-fair city, built out to saturation; the city was a tunnel around the straight-run expressway as it burrowed inwards. A kilometer deep, buried in the center, was the spine around which this organism was built – the Core. As a child, this view had captured him; standing at the base of the Core, he crooked his neck and looked straight up the length of this city's main conduit. It was a thousand meters from earth to roof, a bundled tube of elevators, pipes and columns. Beams splayed out from the core at regular intervals, disappearing into four walls of solid urbanity which defined the shaft's edge. From here it appeared the city supported the Core, but in fact the opposite was true: the beams and columns, designed to support the official city above, were the armature around which this vernacular city had grown.

It had been a long day, but he had some way to travel just yet. Passing through security checkpoints, he reached the glass doors of an elevator, stepped aboard and gazed out as it began to slide upwards. The rhythm of it was hypnotic – a solid wall of humanity which blurred and melded before his eyes as he climbed a thousand meters in two minutes. Stepping off the elevator, he set out towards his ride back down. The Core, the city's busiest transit system, was in truth simply a shuttle between the ground level Arrival Centre and the Topside Transit Hub directly below the roof. The Transit Hub sprawled the width and

breadth of the city, connecting the Core with
a panoply of second-order elevators, tendrils
stretching downward into the flesh of the sub-
city. He lived on the Edges, about four hundred
meters below roof level, but this circuitous route
was his only way home. Access to the roof proper
was strictly limited to Topside residents and their
guests, and was protected by yet another layer of
security and surveillance. He had heard once that
there were other ways to get around - extra-legal
routes up through the Under-city that bypassed the
Core and its surveillance-state nosiness – but he
had never looked into it closely; he was happy to
leave such pursuits to the refugees and smugglers.

Descending alone in his second-order elevator,
he felt a low, distant crack shudder through steel
and concrete. The elevator slowed; red emergency
lights flickering briefly to life before the shaking
subsided and his journey continued. Grown away
from the earth's stable foundation, the city shifted
and settled - tension and release propagating
through its structure in semi-chaotic cycles. Like
a colossal set of lungs or a beating heart, the city
expanded and contracted by design, but recently,
failures had grown in both frequency and severity.
It rattled him to dwell too long on the subject – the
city's mortality and his own, tied up far too close
for comfort.

Stepping off the elevator, he was reassured
by the familiar scene. This was a typical middle-
ring street – lined with small shops and offices,
it formed a convenient thoroughfare for locals on
the route home. Above, the city stretched out
indefinitely, endless layers crossing and recrossing
in the depth. A short way on he came to a wide

passageway and a sliding swipe-card door - he emerged into an enclosed corridor, one wall glazed from floor to ceiling and opening out to a darkened horizon. This development, a new one, was at the absolute Western edge: the long, straight corridor extended the armature of the city, the skeleton around which its next layer would grow.

Sometimes, in the early morning, he would sit out on their balcony. As the sun rose he would watch the city's shadow appear, cast long and low across shallow waters in the West. His breath would catch in his throat, and he would be seized by a paralyzing fear – fear of the monster they had created, two and a half million lives inextricably tangled, waiting for the day the beast would turn on them.

Special Delivery

The truly three-dimensional city is a utopia of free movement. Escape, from whatever pursues you, is trivially easy in this interlocking matrix of rich connections; spatial movement, so closely tied to social control, becomes impossible to regulate.

This did not prevent them from trying - the Topsiders exerted ferocious control in those small areas they could: the Causeway, the Arrival Centre, the Core and the Transit Hub formed a contiguous, tightly governed sequence of spaces linking the Upper City with the outside world – without the correct documents and identification, these sectors were strictly out of bounds.

This was where she came in. Officially, there was only one way for people or goods to move

upwards in this city: through the Core. For those looking to elude the all-seeing eyes of the official city, she was the alternative: somewhere between the Causeway and the Core, a person would disappear into the city's wall-like facade and reappear at the door of her small, unmarked office in the inner sector. The fee subsequently negotiated and payable in advance would cover the passage of either an individual or their goods; it was a hazardous endeavor, so passage wasn't cheap - but it was a damn sight cheaper than getting caught in the Transit Hub with a kilogram

100291

of contraband strapped to your chest. Once she had a destination, she would assign a courier. For common delivery points – the refugee quarter, certain disreputable import/export bazaars – the courier would know the way by heart; in the more far-flung sectors, she would consult her map.

To her way of thinking, she was in the knowledge business. Getting from the bottom of this city to the top wasn't intrinsically difficult – it was a long way up, but gravity provided the essential directions. The real challenge was reaching a specific place efficiently and discreetly - this required local knowledge and connections, and she was a keen collector of both. Officially, there was no complete map of the city. The Topside was scrupulously recorded and the Edges were well documented, but the council had little interest in sending surveyors through the depths of the city. She, on the other hand, had a great deal of interest in mapping – spatial complexity may inhibit spatial control, but spatial freedom can come only from spatial knowledge. Hers was the best map in the city - much of the data she had gathered herself, testing doorways, marking ladders, asking directions. So accurate an accounting of space is a powerful thing: if her competitors got their hands on it, she would be driven out of business - if the Topsiders ever got their hands on it, it would change this city forever.

Her couriers all carried a small device, a hand-held holographic projector jury-rigged by a friend/

debtor of hers. Once activated, the device would display an interactive pathway, the most direct route from A to B, which her couriers had learned to follow religiously. As it stood, the map – the most powerful piece of data in this city's history – was merely a tool, competitive advantage in a money-making game. Its true power – the latent potential to redirect this city's history – remained, for the time being, dormant.

She had been Topside only a half-dozen times - it didn't particularly appeal. She could see the attraction of the sky, the trees and the open space, but it was a bounded domain; all of the edges were hard, and there was nowhere to go but down.

This is the nature of the city – the boundary which excludes also encircles. Every act of segregation, every narrowing of the gate also tightens the noose, drawing the end ever closer. The city is alive. The city is awake. You think that you created it but it, in turn, created you – and one day soon it will throw you from its back and lumber on alone.

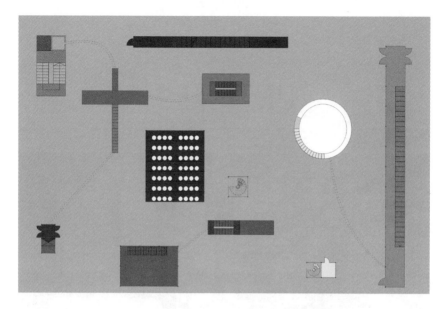

01

02

03

UNTITLED

By Irena Gajic, Tea Belicev & Marta Gajic

Once upon a time there was a boy who lived in a world where everybody had their own house. The houses weren't ordinary houses. No. These were houses that you could not abandon. The boy's house went with him wherever he would go. He would play with it and change its shape, color... Oh, how fun it was to have that house! "See those sad plants and animals they don't have their own houses to play with like me."

One day a tree appeared in front of the boy's house:

"Knock, knock," a sound was heard on the boy's door.

"Who could that be" the boy inquired as he went to the door. When the boy opened the door he set his eyes upon a tree that looked tired and was missing a couple of its branches.

"Please, would you be so kind as to bring me some water", said the tree. "I have been traveling for days and haven't had anything to drink."

The boy invited the tree into his house, gave him a chair to sit and brought him a pitcher full of water.

"Does it hurt?" asked the boy, nodding towards the place where branches once sprouted.

"A little bit, but they'll grow back though".

"Will they grow back by tomorrow?" asked the boy excitedly.

The tree laughed warmly at the boy's question. It had to explain that it takes a lot of time, sunshine and water for a branch to grow. That gave the boy an idea.

"Why don't you stay with me until your branches grow back? I have a lot of water. Your branches will easily grow back."

The tree pondered on the boy's suggestion: "The boy is right I've been traveling for a long time and its time that I got some rest and recovered a bit."

"You know what, it's time that I rest and recuperate, and the company would also do me some good. I've had so many wonderful experiences during my travels it would be nice to have somebody to share them with."

"How interesting it will be to have somebody else in the house. And not anybody else, but a tree! A tree that will share its experiences with me! I will have to change the house to better suit a tree, to give him water, sunshine..." thought the boy.

Night had fallen outside and it was time to sleep.

"Tomorrow I'll have to get a comfortable bed for the tree and I have to find a way to let as much sunshine into the house, and..." but the boy was tired and drifted into a sleep before he could finish his thought.

In the morning the tree was woken by the sun that bathed its bark in light. It got out of bed and as it did so the boy came into the room.

"Good morning", said the tree.

"Oh, good morning", replied the boy "I've brought you this flowerpot. We'll fill here with earth. When the rain falls I'll collect the water so that you'll never be thirsty again. Consider this room yours and I'll do my best that not a single branch of yours breaks again."

"Thank you dear boy! No one has ever done so much for me", said the tree gratefully.

The boy and the tree got along splendidly. The boy enjoyed taking care of the tree and adapting the house towards him, and the tree enjoyed the care he was given as well as the boy's company. Sometimes, when the wind would blow, the tree would vividly recount his travels to the boy.

"Far away exists a city where people live without houses. That city is very well protected. It has two gates at the entrance that only some may pass."

As time passed the tree sprouted new branches. The boy grew afraid that the tree would leave him, so one night while the tree slept the boy trapped the tree within a cylinder.

"Why have you done this?" asked the tree when he woke up.

"I don't want you to leave. Who would tell me

stories if you leave?"

"You should not be angry, we had an agreement. I am grateful to you but as you know I have to move on."

The boy knew that the tree was right. He removed the cylinder and let the tree sleep in peace, in the morning they said their goodbyes, as true friends, and the tree left. The boy felt very lonely in his house. He collected water and made an entire room covered in earth. Now that the tree had gone he had no reason to keep it. "What use is such a house to me?" he asked himself and then remembered the tree's story of the city without houses and thought how they certainly don't have those kinds of problems there. "I should seek out this city. It must be better there!"

He packed his things and, with his house, went to search for the city.

Along the way everything that he saw seemed familiar. The tree really knew how to make you feel as if you where there when it told its stories. One thing did turn up that the tree didn't mention in his tales. It was a wall. Enormous, long and filled with blinking eyes. The boy couldn't go around, nor jump over it. It had a gate so high up that he was unable to reach it and long narrow stairs that were impossible to climb. The boy took a few steps back, sat on the ground and stared at the wall. As he looked upon it he started not to care about how he would traverse it. The longer he looked at it the more mesmerized he became. Hours passed and

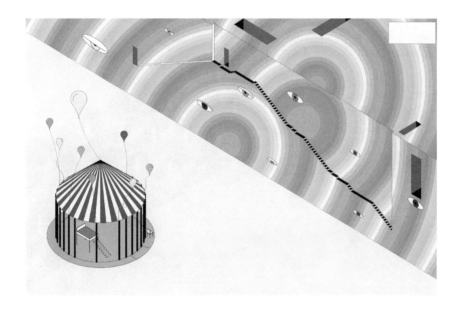

he still stared. Suddenly the wall disappeared and a road came to sight in front of the boy. He decided to take the road and later arrived at a meadow in the middle of which a large wall arose. As he approached he noticed that inside the walls there was an incredible amount of stairs which tied onto one another in an almost endless chain. The boy went around the walls, but he was unable to find the entrance until he found a small opening. He tried to go through it, but it was too narrow. Whichever way he tried, he couldn't succeed. He realized that the house was what was keeping him from going through.

"There must be another way, perhaps there is a rope I can use to climb up and over the walls", thought the boy. He looked around but there was no rope. He sat and started thinking.

"There is no way I'll enter like this. I'll have to make my house much smaller."

The boy got rid of all the things that were too big to pass through the hole and shrank his house. When he went through the opening he saw a multitude of stairs laid out before him and he didn't know where to go. He looked at a sign beside him; it showed him to go right, so he did. He climbed up the stairs following the signs until suddenly he found himself right back where he started.

"I must have taken a wrong turn", the boy decided to try again and once more he found himself where he started.

"Something must be wrong with these signs.

Why am I even following them?"

The boy resolved to go opposite of the way shown on the signs. Instead of left, he went right, instead of up, he went down, sometimes upside down, sometimes right side up, and after awhile he stumbled upon a door in the floor. He opened the door and took a peek through it. All around him were people floating in the air with their heads facing down. He realized right away that this was the city about which the tree had told him. He was very excited, never had he seen anything like this. Everyone was gently floating in the air like clouds. He turned to the person nearest to him and said: "Its really wonderful here", the person didn't even turn around to face him, he floated silently.

"Hm, this one doesn't seem to be very talkative."

"It's really nice here. You must not have any worries", he turned to a different person. The other one also didn't react.

"The people sure are impolite towards their guests", noted the boy, but soon he realized that they didn't even talk with each other.

"It really is boring here!" said the boy out loud, but even then nobody moved a muscle. "It was nice to have met you, but I think I'll leave."

The boy didn't know where to go from there but it didn't matter, the only thing he knew was that wherever he went he was on the right track.

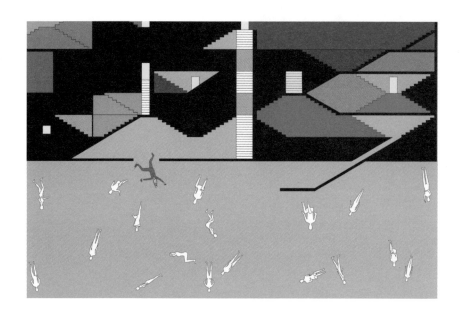

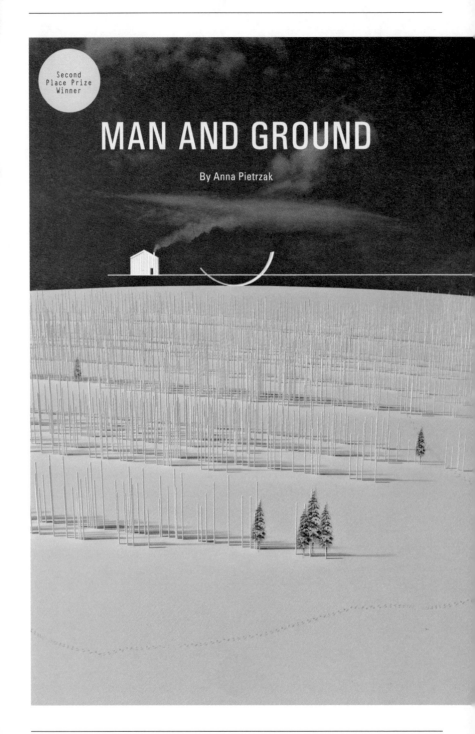

Second
Place Prize
Winner

MAN AND GROUND

By Anna Pietrzak

There is a constant presence in man's life
The presence of ground

Ground is curved
Ground is fluid
Ground is surface
Ground receives man's shadow
Ground receives man's body.
Man knows ground through building
Building is dialogue; a story that lives in work
Ground asks questions to building
Building demands answers from ground
Architecture is language.

I.

Ground as Curve

The ground is curved.
The man is a vertical being
who lives on this curve.
He stands perpendicular to its surface.

As he walks along the curve, his
movement traces concentric rings.
No matter how far his body travels, it
shares one angle with the ground.
He is a spoke rotated each day by the curve.
The horizon surrounds him. But it deceives.
It wants him to perceive its edge
as the end of the world.
But he knows from walking that
this edge moves as he moves...
and thus the ground has no end.

The horizon mocks and the
curve promises sameness,
but the man seeks new experience with ground.

He builds his own curve; it mirrors
the shape of the ground.
Upon this inverted curve he places a line.
The line is unique; it is tangent.

To live on this line would be his wish.
And thus, upon the line he builds his home.
But the dream has a dilemma...

If man and home are to unite on the line, they
must meet at the fulcrum.
Yet, to rest at the fulcrum, both man and home
would once more lie perpendicular to ground.

He must sacrifice.
To walk the tangent, he must leave his home.
The weight of the home counters
the weight of the man.
Both rest apart from one another upon the line.
They suspend in equilibrium.
They suspend in tension.

Fluid Ground
Man builds a tower. He escapes the ground.

He climbs the tower. He feels tired. He
experiences weight.

As he moves upward, something pulls;
An invisible force begging him down.
The pull comes from the great
mass of the ground.
He ascends, balanced at the peak of the tower...
Suspended in delicate equilibrium.
He exists between the climb and the fall.
He exists between past and future.
He is present... frozen in a moment of anticipation.

Then, he jumps.
His body weightless, falling, falling, falling free...
Parallel with gravity.

Splash.
The undisturbed plane is broken, he dives through
the liquid surface.
He has fallen into the ground.

He climbs again. But soon he tires...
He rotates the vertical tower.
It forms a ramp. Making his movement now
gradual and slow.
He does not leap but glides into the depths
of the ground.
He lies on the ramp as if it were a shore, allowing
the ground to wash itself upon him.
He lies passive. The ground submerges him
at its will, not his.

Life happens as a single unbroken day.

III.

Ground as Surface
The ground is flat. The ground is surface.
But how can he know?
He could chase the horizon; run to its edge...
But the surface of the ground is long and wide;
longer and wider than the length of his life.
Could there be a shorter path?
...not around the plane, but through it?
The ground is flat. The ground is surface.
To pierce the surface, is to see the other side;
is to free the other side.

He builds a tool; a pendulum.
Pushing and releasing, he draws
a line to dig a path.
The line is drawn on top of itself again
and again and again...
The series of lines yield a great cavernous space.

As onlookers peer high above at the pivot,
They measure his efforts, counting each cycle
of the swinging plow.
Work, worker, and place never separate.
He deposits himself into the place,
through the work.
He shapes the space. He finds purpose...

IV.

It begins... protocol is rule, protocol is order.
The man builds a grid; the spatial
manifestation of order.
The work is monotonous; alas,
a field of sameness.
Can't he be free? What would it mean to be
free... to break convention?

In his daily patterns, he observes
the directions of the grid;
His body vertical by day, horizontal by night.
But he rises one morning with the sun and finds a
new direction.

He sees the line of his shadow.
It breaks the grid, free and changing
throughout the day.
He is fascinated by the line; it becomes his
obsession.

He studies the line of his shadow.
Exploring its many angles, given
to him each day by the sun.
He must capture this line.
It should persist long after the sun has set.
It should persist after he no longer exists to cast

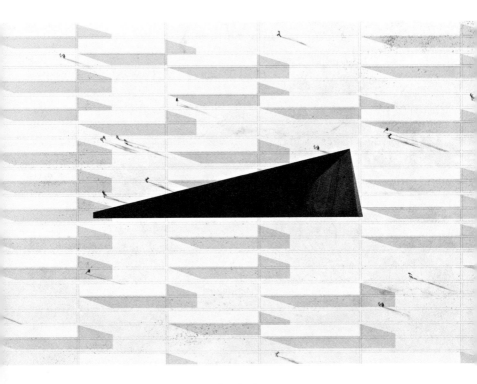

the shadow.
This line will be a diagonal.
It will be positioned within the grid, but will
oppose its framework.
He will build a triangle... a diagonal enclosure.
He will build a void... a mass of shadow.

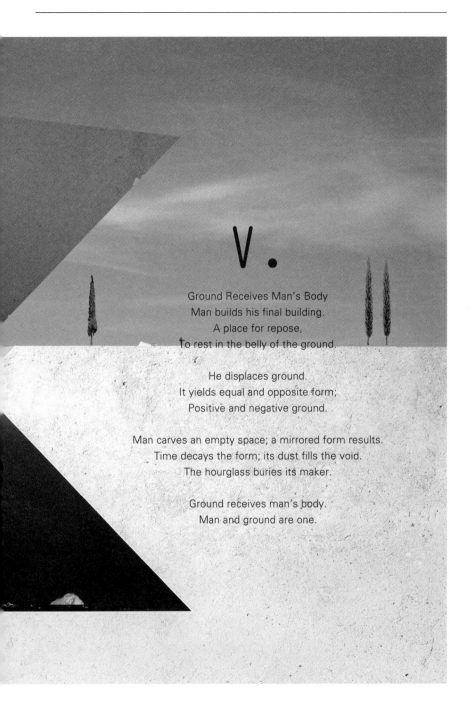

V.

Ground Receives Man's Body

Man builds his final building.
A place for repose,
To rest in the belly of the ground.

He displaces ground.
It yields equal and opposite form;
Positive and negative ground.

Man carves an empty space; a mirrored form results.
Time decays the form; its dust fills the void.
The hourglass buries its maker.

Ground receives man's body.
Man and ground are one.

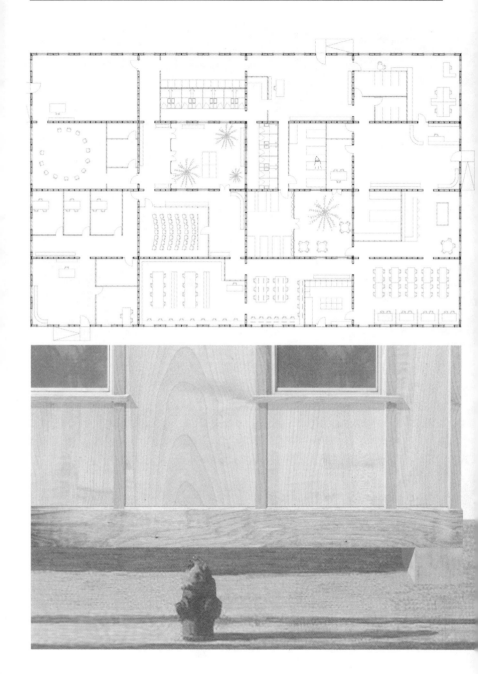

BEGGAR'S BANQUET

By Antoine Collet Architect D.E.

This story tries to meld reality and fiction. This story uses the depth of reality to bring dreams into our simple daily life. This story is about architecture.

The American Beggars Banquet Foundation intended to build a day-care center in Brooklyn. This building offered all services homeless people needed. Showers, resting rooms, cafés, people to talk to, a laundry room, an address, the internet, washing machines: everything for free. They were open during the day and anyone could come in.

The construction had to be cheap and easy to transport and rebuild. It was a simple wooden structure like an 18th century balloon frame, although it used nuts and bolts instead of nails. The plan was made up of 7m by 12m rectangular rooms. Partition walls were used to create smaller rooms as needed.

The plan of the first building in Brooklyn looked like a labyrinth even though it was not. It was more like a Temple that opened its four façades to the outside. The building was divided into four areas:

1. A reception center, an internet café and a reading room
2. Bathrooms, laundry and rest rooms
3. Space for the neighborhood association
4. A counseling center

These areas were linked by two patios. Both could be used separately or together. The plan offered intimacy and places for people to meet. All sorts of people came to the Beggars Banquet Foundation: homeless and poor people looking for a job, lonely

people, neighbors, young travelers, fighting men and curious passers-by.

The Beggars Banquet Foundation was constantly seeking free places in New York to install their centers. Any kind of place could be chosen thanks to the light structure of the center. In Dumbo for instance, next to the Hudson River, a building was about to be destroyed, but instead, the roof was donated to the foundation to install public baths. The space was very simple. There were only showers and bathrooms and a garden in front of the Hudson River. This building offered big bathrooms and an open view. People could enjoy a pure private moment facing the Manhattan skyline. Naked while facing Wall Street!

More and more centers were built in New York City. The Beggars Banquet Foundation needed a head office! A free corner plot was found on Central Park South. The tiny building was separated in two parts. One was an administrative office to manage the centers and create helpful maps and tips to find food, clothing and facilities. The other part held exhibitions. The foundation wanted to tell New Yorkers about this existing parallel life in their city. One day the foundation organized an architecture exhibition about all the recent projects. One of these architects exhibited a drawing of the Koolhaas floating swimming pool. A few days after the exhibition had started, an old man came and stopped in front of this picture. After a while he asked the volunteer:

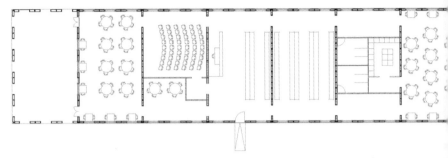

« - Are you still looking for a site to build another center?

-Yes we are. The amount of people needing help is still increasing, you know?

-Fortunately, more and more volunteers want to help us. I was one of these guys in the street, and now I am one of the Beggars Banquet members!

-If so, I think I can help by giving you something... »

This old man was, indeed, an important art collector. He was also the owner of an old floating swimming pool that he had bought from the Russians a few decades ago. He never used the swimming pool; it was still docked in Red Hook as a forgotten ruin of an old delirious fairy tale. To give new life to the floating pool, the collector chose to give it to the Beggars Banquet Foundation.

The boat was retrofitted to offer free public transportation between the centers. Tourists and New Yorkers, attracted by this strange barge, also used it to discover a new way of life in the huge city.

Finally, homeless people, as members of the Beggars Banquet Foundation, became the new guides of New York City.

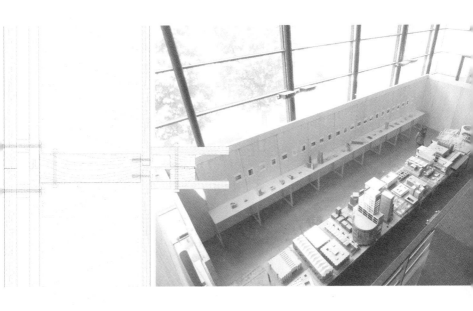

IVY GIRL & THE CLOVERLEAF

By S. H. Fumanelli and T. J. Surjan

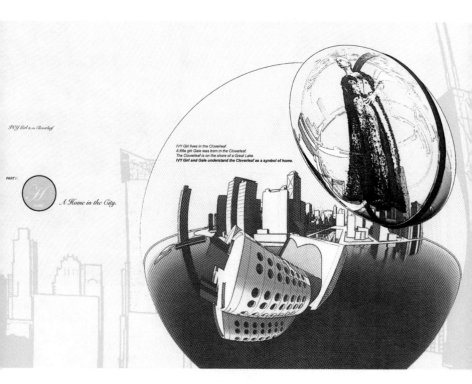

IVY Girl lives in the Cloverleaf.
A little girl Gale was born in the Cloverleaf.
The Cloverleaf is on the shore of a Great Lake.
IVY Girl and Gale understand the Cloverleaf as a symbol of home.

PART I.

A Home in the City.

Part I : HOME

IVY Girl lives in the Cloverleaf.
A little girl Gale was born in the Cloverleaf.
The Cloverleaf is on the shore of a Great Lake.
IVY Girl and Gale understand the Cloverleaf as a
symbol of home.

Gale walks past the site of her birthplace
regularly just to see her beloved Cloverleaf.

One day on her walk she returned to the
Cloverleaf and her birthplace had vanished.

Part II : VOID

"Where did my Cloverleaf go?" said Gale to
herself.

Gale went home and asked her parents where
the Cloverleaf had gone. She learned that the
owner of the site sank the Cloverleaf into the Great
Lake. The owner of the site decided a new shiny
building is needed to replace it.

Her parents said it was impossible to bring back
the Cloverleaf. The Cloverleaf was an engineering
marvel, but it is old and out of date now. They also
explained to Gale why she felt so attached to the

Cloverleaf. You're old enough now to understand something we have never told you before. Gale, the day you were born something unfortunate happened. Your mother passed away giving birth to you. We adopted you when you were only two days old. The Cloverleaf is a symbol of the union of our family. It is also a symbol of life to all the citizens in the city. We have been walking past the Cloverleaf for years and telling you her story for all these reasons.

"I understand," said Gale.

"I also understand the Cloverleaf needs to be remembered," said Gale.

After dinner that night, Gale went to bed not knowing what to do about the Cloverleaf.

"Who can help me bring back the Cloverleaf?" said Gale to herself.

Gale awoke during the night and decided she needed to return to the Cloverleaf site at once. The site was still the same as before, completely absent of the Cloverleaf. As Gale decided to say goodbye for the last time, she heard something.

"Who's there?" said Gale.

Gale did not hear a response, and just put the noise to something in the March wind. As she turned to leave the site, she was startled by a voice asking her "Who's there?" Gale began running and ran all the way back to her house.

The next morning Gale was wondering if it all was a dream or if her imagination was playing tricks of her. At school that day she told her

classmates about the voice she heard at the
Cloverleaf site, but no one believed her story.
Gale returned home after school more troubled
than the day before. She decided to return to the
site once again after her parents were asleep.
Returning to the Cloverleaf site would prove to
her that no one was there. In her heart, Gale
didn't know if she wanted that to be true.

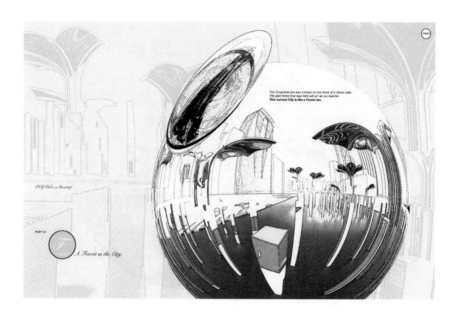

Part III : FOREST

Gale walked very slowly in the dark to the
Cloverleaf site. Her pace was slow as she pondered
what she would find this night. She arrived to find
the site unchanged from the night before. The void

created by the missing building was now twofold. One, in that the building was gone and not coming back. Two, because she felt a void within herself as well. Gale was lamenting the Cloverleaf.

After a few moments, Gale decided to try something. She decided to speak, but to speak only one word.

"Hello?" said Gale.

Almost instantaneously a voice replied "Good to see you again".

Gale thought to run as she did the night before. This night she stood perfectly still.

"Who's there?" said Gale.

"IVY Girl," said the voice.

"I can't see you," said Gale.

"Can you see my sphere?" said IVY Girl.

"I can see a green dress, is that you?" said Gale.

"Yes, I was born here long before the Cloverleaf was built," said IVY Girl.

"Where do you live now that the Cloverleaf is gone?" said Gale.

"I live just offshore in the Great Lake," said IVY Girl.

"Is that what your sphere is for?" said Gale.

"Exactly, it floats very well," said IVY Girl.

"So, are we both here for the same reason?" asked Gale.

"I hope so," said IVY Girl.

"Do you know if we can bring the Cloverleaf back?" said Gale.

"Yes, to some extent," said IVY Girl.

"What to do you mean?" said Gale.

"We first need to talk about why we want to bring back the Cloverleaf," said IVY Girl.

"Ok, I'm listening," said Gale.

"You should sit down Gale, I have a story to tell you," said IVY Girl.

The story begins over three centuries ago. The Cloverleaf site was a forest on the shore of a Great Lake. This was long before a city would grow in and around this site as well. The past forest that was here will act as our teacher. This current City is like a Forest too. Think of each building in the city as a tree. Many of the trees in the city seem identical. Cutting down one tree is similar to cutting down any tree. Therefore, cutting down one building is similar to cutting down any building. Only, this is not true. The Cloverleaf was cut down, but it was not any tree. The reason for this is simple. The Cloverleaf was not just a building. The Cloverleaf was an Architecture. Architecture is thinking plus building, not building without thinking. Cutting down some trees makes the forest healthier. Cutting down the entire forest is wrong. The Cloverleaf was the Queen of her forest. The heir to her throne was also born in the Cloverleaf. Gale, you are the heir to the throne of her forest. It is your responsibility to preserve the Cloverleaf.

As IVY Girl concluded the story she left one last important detail. Bringing back the Cloverleaf would be like planting a new tree. The new tree would be similar, but not identical to the Cloverleaf.

Gale thought for a minute, embracing the meaning of the story.

"I don't want to plant a tree, I want to plant a forest," said Gale.

"I'm so glad you understood the story," said IVY Girl.

Gale then said she had a wish to ask of IVY Girl.

Her wish was to grow a Cloverleaf forest.

"Is this an impossible wish?" asked Gale.

"No, to wish for the impossible is a great place to start," said IVY Girl.

Gale's wish would take all of IVY Girl's magical powers. The owner of the site was starting construction the next morning. Her wish needed to be completed in a single night.

Part IV : MEMORY

Gale's parents woke her very early the next morning. She was told they needed to go for a walk immediately. Gale got dressed and off they went. Outside it seemed that everyone was headed in the same direction. As Gale looked ahead, she saw where everyone was headed. A Cloverleaf forest had grown during the night. A crowd gathered in awe of the Cloverleaf forest. The owner of the site was also impressed by the magnitude of the new structures.

"Who did this?" said the Owner.

"I know who did this," said Gale.

"Who???" said the owner.

"IVY Girl did this," said Gale.

"Who's Ivy Girl?" said the Owner.

"IVY Girl is my mother," said Gale.

The crowd that gathered began to cheer.
Gale's parent's eyes filled with tears of joy. The
Cloverleaf forest is a living model of preservation.
Preservation of both a memory and of Architecture.
IVY Girl made Gale's wish into a reality.

Part V : WISH

Gale slipped away from the crowd, to the edge
of the Great Lake. Gale had one more wish to ask
of IVY Girl. Gale wished that the entire city be made
a forest for a single day. Her wish was to return the
city to the forest it once was long ago.

"The City is like a forest," said IVY Girl.

"Cloverleaf is our home," said Gale.

IVY Girl told Gale she would grant her wish, with
one exception.

"What is the exception?" said Gale.

"You must grant me a wish." said IVY Girl.

IVY Girl's wish was that Gale build a new
Cloverleaf with her daughter one day.

"I will," said Gale.

As Gale left, she paused to say one last thing to
IVY Girl.

"Goodnight Mom," said Gale.

As Gale fell asleep that night she was thinking

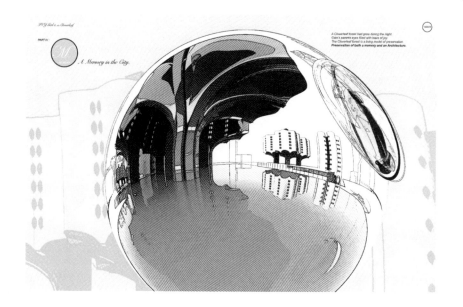

of the lessons IVY Girl had taught her. The City is like a forest, but not all trees in the forest are alike. The wish made in a fairy tale is the beginning of an Architecture. The Queen of the Cloverleaf forest slept very well embracing her two new lessons.

The next morning, Gale awoke to her vision of the city.

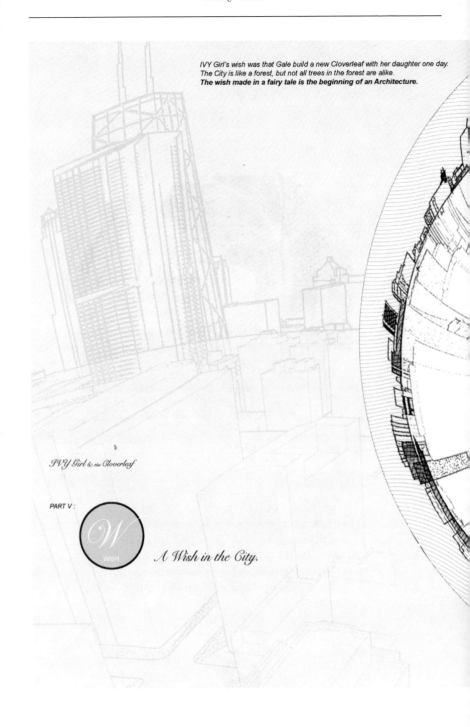

IVY Girl's wish was that Gale build a new Cloverleaf with her daughter one day.
The City is like a forest, but not all trees in the forest are alike.
The wish made in a fairy tale is the beginning of an Architecture.

IVY Girl & the Cloverleaf

PART V :

W
WISH

A Wish in the City.

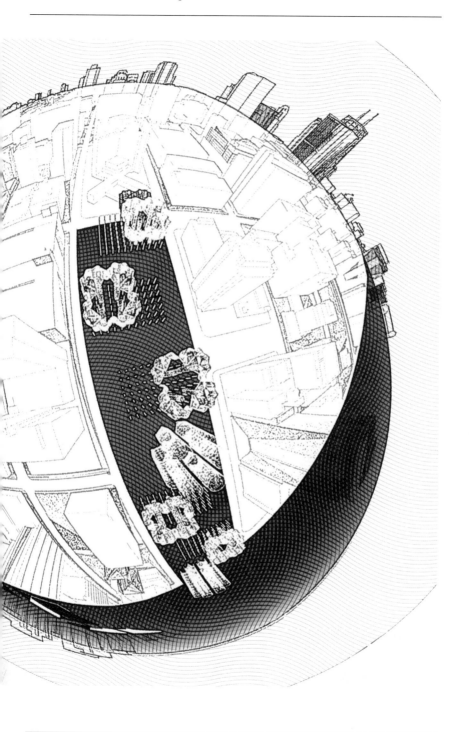

AWAY WITH THE FAIRIES

By J.P. Maruszczak, Roger Connah & Ryan Manning

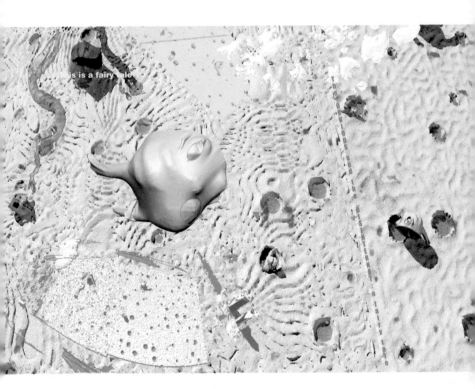

Part 1: The Obvious and the Disinternet: a fairytale

(sound: a brief burst of The Beatles
"I am the Walrus"
without paying copyright fees)

Expert textpert choking smokers,
Don't you think the joker laughs at you?
See how they smile like pigs in a sty,
See how they snide, I'm crying.

And where am I coming from that I am addressing
you so: the high arctic, the low arctic, the middle
arctic? Or the faux arctic? The land that is not
is about to be penetrated; the visitor is given a
seal suit and polar bear trousers. The pure bardo
of landscape is up for grabs. The whiteout is
protected by expensive sunglasses, as we follow
the cameraman in search of - quote - the iconic of
all arctic animals, the walrus – end of quote!

This is a fairy tale.

I dream sentences. I always have done. They
are uninhabited landscapes, fairy tales until we
commit to them, until – like the Arctic - we impose
ourselves
on them.
Sometimes I force myself to wake and write them
down. Other times, in the morning, I may have
forgotten I even had or thought those sentences.
Or then I try and remember. It never works.

Usually the note is written in half-sleep, difficult
to decode. This one was less difficult. It was after
I received a note about the 'changing landscape'.
The note was crude but beautiful: basically, the
ice is melting, the resources in the Arctic are
up for grabs…"it's serious, we need to meet,"
someone had said.

Then I dreamed, I fairytaled, my sentence: We are
dealing with the obvious and the disinternet.

That is not how a fairy tale works.

So what could these two words mean or signify?
The Obvious and the Disinternet? Are they
connected to this vast region, this changing
landscape? And how? Is this the 'arctic of the
imagination' described by the intrepid broadcaster,
Bruce Parry? Is it this interconnectivity that goes
before us, seduces us; in a region, apparently
untouchable for so long, but where many ideas
are lying dormant, where many ideas have been

uttered before? In a region where visions have
been forgotten but not necessarily undermined,
only to be shockingly relevant right now. And
when, in this changing landscape - is right now?
Only to be right now again, 10, 20 or 30 years on?
We must fairy tale this obviousness.
The obvious asks another question. If we can
re-situate this knowledge, perhaps if we can
all re-situate our knowledge, if we can suggest
why inter-connectedness should work when it
doesn't, why our awareness meets the buffers
of unpredictability, political initiatives against
economic realities, we might just, I repeat just,
meet the obvious from another angle.

A Fairy tale must be unpredictable.

We may always need to defer to such experts
who will warn us of the future. And if we are not
to become the people we warn ourselves against,
we may need to accept our own undermining of
the very fragility of the present, as we find new
ways to award new relevance.

Is this also not Obvious? Not a fairy tale?

But the fairy tale of the Obvious

In 1967 at the Roundhouse in Chalk farm London
The Congress on the Dialectics of Liberation was
held. The organizing group came from a group
of radical thinkers and innovators especially in
the field of psychiatry, perhaps the most well
known amongst them, the Scottish psychiatrist

R D Laing and the South African David Cooper. Existential psychiatrists, Marxist thinkers, anarchists, philosophers and politicians met to take on this issue: Stokely Carmichael, Geoffrey Bateson, Jules Henry, Paul Goodman, Lucien Goldman and Herbert Marcuse.

"It is obvious, R.D. Laing wrote, that the social world situation is endangering the future of all life on this planet." Laing's paper was called The Obvious. We can juggle the words around and we would neatly include the Arctic in our threatened future. "To state the obvious" Laing went on to say, "is to share with you what (in your view) my misconceptions might be. The obvious can be dangerous. The deluded man (or woman!) frequently finds his (or her) delusion so obvious that he can hardly credit the good faith of those who do not share them." The key phrase for me, and one which I think we can lift across the years to this changing landscape, is as follows; "I shall have to deal for the most part in generalities. I am not sure whether these are clichés to many of you. One man's revolution is another's platitude."

How can we turn the Obvious to our advantage?

The Dialectics of Liberation, something we might say we are still contemplating, was a phrase immediately challenged by the philosopher Marcuse as being somewhat tautological. For all dialectic he suggested was by nature 'liberating'. The obvious perhaps needs re-stating. To try and understand in all awareness of impending change and the landscape, in all our understanding of the notion of the arctic frontier, we too often meet situations where our 'dialectic' – our attempts to go back and forth in liberating openness – remain strangely fixed, and dare we say, in this context 'frozen' by that other fairy tale, The Disinternet.

So to the Disinternet?
What fairy tale is this?

The Disinternet? What does it mean, what could it mean? What could it mean here when we start to re-value the opposition that nature offers us? Seal Hunting, reindeer herding and Zinc mining.

For the Disinternet is that which derails the obvious. In the arctic fairy tale this may mean the issues we attempt - often brilliantly - to talk about in a major way.

The Disinternet is the new hacker ethic, the constant way knowledge – shall we accept alertness rather than knowledge - can be disclaimed, disinterred, shifted and distrusted by the very openness of the shifting ground before us. It is the reverse of insinuation: a self-canceling desire that continually calls for action (think of Haiti 2010 to Haiti 2013) but eliminates that call or action in the disclaimed world. We wish to impose without imposition.

It's obvious; this is a shocking dilemma, too.
Fairy Tales are shocking dilemmas, too.

That is why this is a fairy tale from the Land that is Not.

The region that is no place is hardly a new idea, but it has a Nordic if not an Arctic resonance. The Finnish poet Paavo Haavikko continued the utterance of the Finnish Swedish poet Edith Sodergran who journeyed at the start of the 20th century, in her language and landscape, to the land that is not. In the Third poem of one of the most appreciated but forgotten poems of the last century The Winter Palace, we get the sense of where our changing landscape emerges:

I came through the forest and went through the Winter Palace
Built in 1754-1762.
I let the exalted being out of the bottle and she
Was finished! Emptied! Aborted!
I am on the way to the region that is no place,
Listen, you who like climbing monuments,
Tourist, listen, perhaps you don't even know
I hardly get my expenses back, writing these poems, on
My way
To the region that is no place.

Where is this region that celebrates its nothingness with the urgency of lives about to be lost in development and progress? What is this fairy tale that ever re-writes the changing mind of the imagination defined by awareness and activism – whose livelihood will be restricted?

The seal hunters, the polar bear hunters of Sarnak,
North Greenland, finding less and less to hunt, as
the landscape warms up, spring thaws unevenly,
as the waters close on previously safe and known
hunting regions. 6 polar bears can be killed or
5 narwahl, that medium-sized toothed whale –
predator is turned predator - meaning that the
hunter must enter the local supermarket in Sarnak
to buy lamb for example: 5 chops for 35 pounds
or 50 Euro. The figures vary of course but the
message is clear. As the polar bears tracked by
spy cam have to swim longer and search longer
to reach the drifting ice floes, the explorer strips
blubber for a snack and the fly in fly out model of
mining, or the temporary mining communities re-
buried into the very mine of Nanisivik confuses the
narrative of that 'place where one finds things'.

The black walrus is a fairy tale. ....I am he as you
are he as you are me and we are all together/ See
how they run like pigs from a gun, see how they
fly. I'm crying. Perhaps it is too easy to snipe at the
broadcaster eating Narwhal blubber or raw seal's
liver, washed down with the jelly of a seal's eye. We
live in the consumption of this awareness whilst we
encounter the obvious every moment.

Away with the fairies,
we live the fairy tale behind us.

150

AT 150 ASTRONOMICAL UNITS FROM THE EARTH, HUMANKIND'S FARTHEST SPACE PROBE – PROGRAMMED TO DISTANCE ITSELF FROM THE EARTH INDEFINITELY – WAS HALTED.

CRUST

By Chanel Dehond

At precisely 150 astronomical units from the Earth, humankind's farthest space probe was halted. The Deep Space Network received radio waves transmitting the space probe's collision with an unforeseen mass. The reverberant sound of the collision was unbearably great, though – in the vacuum of the universe – unheard.

On this interstellar mission for the advancement of human knowledge, the space probe was programmed to continuously distance itself from the Earth's surface. In the case of confrontation, this 1.5 tonne apparatus would recalibrate its trajectory to complete its mission.

Error *shoooop* *beep boop beep* *click* —— Error *shoooop* *beep boop beep* *click* —— Error *shoooop* *beep boop beep* *click* —— Error *shoooop* *beep boop beep* *click* —— Error *shoooop* *beep boop beep* *click* —— Error *shoooop* *beep boop beep* *click* —— Error *shoooop* *beep boop beep* *click* —— Error *shoooop* *beep boop beep* *click* —— - Error *shoooop* *beep boop beep* *click* —— Error *shoooop* *beep boop beep* *click* —— Error *shoooop* *beep boop beep* *click* —— Error *shoooop* *beep boop beep* *click* —— Error *shoooop* *beep boop beep* *click* —— Error *shoooop* *beep boop beep* *click* —— Error *shoooop* *beep boop beep* *click* —— Error *shoooop* *beep boop beep* *click* —— Error *shoooop* *beep boop beep* *click* —— Error *shoooop* *beep boop beep* *click* —— Error *shoooop* *beep boop beep* *click* —— Error *shoooop* *beep boop beep* *click* —— Error *shoooop* *beep boop beep* *click* —— Error *shoooop* *beep boop beep* *click* —— Error *shoooop* *beep boop beep* *click* —— Error *shoooop* *beep boop beep* *click* —— ∞

THE BOUNDARY PERSISTED
INFINITELY, AT THE GIVEN RADIUS
FROM THE EARTH, AND THIS WAS
MADE THE GREATEST HUMAN
DISCOVERY TO DATE.

THE DISCOVERY OF A CRUST,
SURROUNDING THE SOLAR
SYSTEM

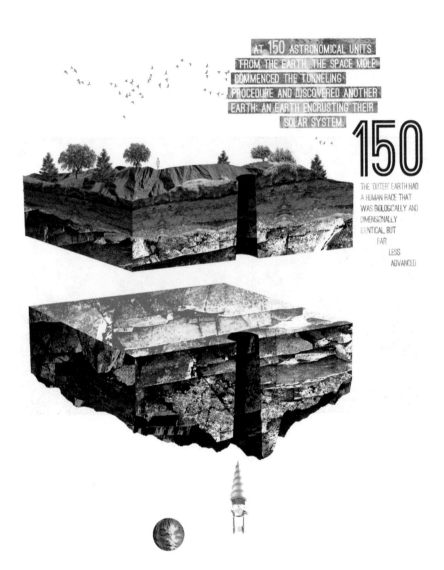

AT 150 ASTRONOMICAL UNITS FROM THE EARTH, THE SPACE MOLE COMMENCED THE TUNNELING PROCEDURE AND DISCOVERED ANOTHER EARTH: AN EARTH ENCRUSTING THEIR SOLAR SYSTEM.

150

THE 'OUTER' EARTH HAD A HUMAN RACE THAT WAS BIOLOGICALLY AND DIMENSIONALLY IDENTICAL BUT FAR LESS ADVANCED

The boundary persisted infinitely, at the given radius (precisely 150 astronomical units) from the Earth, and thus was made the greatest human discovery to date – the discovery that changed the perception of the entire race - the discovery of a crust surrounding the solar system.

A paradoxical conundrum presented itself; the Earthlings lusted to expand their understanding of the universe, but retracted with fear of the unknown. The pros and cons – for tunneling through the crust – were weighed;

Pro: the answer to the ultimate question of life, the universe, and everything could be beyond the crust.

Con: humanity could be sucked into a black hole.

Con: the crust could be impenetrable.

Con: the crust could be infinite.

Con: the solar system could explode.

Con: the solar system could deflate.

Con: the plug could be pulled and the fluid – in which the solar system floats – could be released, drowning the entire galaxy.

Con: the portal to hell could be unlocked.

Con: the force field, protecting the solar system, could be penetrated.

Con: destructive extra-terrestrials could infiltrate the solar system.

Con: humanity could discover that they existed within a beaker on a shelf of supplementary beakers.

Con: God could confound their speech, so that they could not understand each other, and scatter

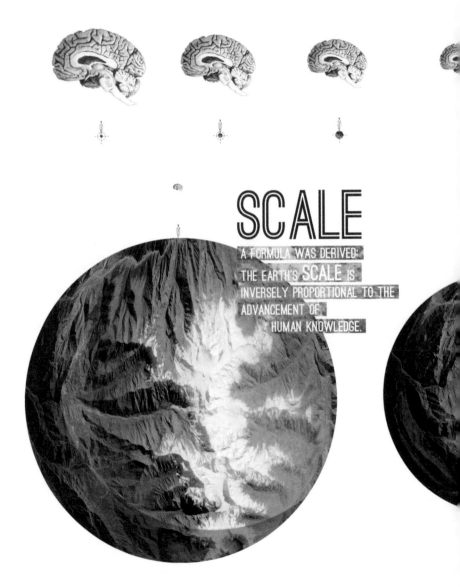

SCALE

A FORMULA WAS DERIVED:
THE EARTH'S **SCALE** IS
INVERSELY PROPORTIONAL TO THE
ADVANCEMENT OF
HUMAN KNOWLEDGE.

them globally.

Con: there could be a barbaric giant, who recites, "fee-fi-fo-fum!"

Con: humanity could be living on a speck, on a clover, held by an elephant.

And so, despite the unbalanced nature of this exercise, mankind's curiosity prevailed and the unanimous decision was made to tunnel through the crust.

At precisely 150 astronomical units from the Earth, the space mole – containing surveillance technologies – commenced the tunneling procedure. Aboard the craft was audio-visual evidence of the Earth, in the event that it came into contact with extra-terrestrial life. Humanity waited tensely.

The breakthrough

inhale.

The silence was deafening *exhale*. Not ever was there an incident so indiscriminate.

The space mole began transmitting images of the Earth, to the Earth. The population erupted in confusion as the space mole was not designed to broadcast the "enclosed evidence" homeward. This however, was not the "enclosed evidence".

The reality of the broadcast did not resonate immediately. Mankind was, unknowingly, gazing upon another Earth; an Earth encrusting their Solar System. This Earth had humans – a human race outside of their human race, on an Earth, precisely 150 astronomical units, outside of their Earth.

Further analysis determined that the "outer" human race was biologically and dimensionally identical to the "inner", though far less advanced. The following formula was derived:

$$\text{Earth's Scale} \propto \frac{1}{\textit{Advancement of Human Knowledge}}$$

In layman's terms; an Earth's scale is inversely proportional to the advancement of human knowledge (e.g. if a human could walk around the Earth in a day, they could know the entirety of things much quicker than a human who took 802,701 years to walk a different Earth).

The complexity of this circumstance broadened exponentially as the truth revealed itself. The answer to the ultimate question of life, the universe, and everything was indeed beyond the crust – beyond innumerable crusts. Yet, just beyond the "outer" Earth – beyond both Earths – were innumerable Earths. Innumerable Earths with men still unknowing, existing as Russian nesting dolls in a limitless set.

BEYOND BOTH EARTHS WERE
INNUMERABLE EARTHS, EXISTING AS
RUSSIAN NESTING DOLLS
IN A LIMITLESS SET.

DETROIT S.A.R.

the Land of the
Chinese God of Wealth

DETROIT S.A.R.

By Ya Suo & Rania Ghosn

18, 2013
roit Bankruptcy

Jun 2014
Bilateral Meeting Negotiating
Trade between US and China

恭喜發財

Don't Show Me
the Money
SHOW ME
THE MONET

THE ART
BELONGS TO
THE PEOPLE
NOT THE RICH

Jul 1, 2015
The Establishment of Detroit S.A.R.

Oct 4, 2023
Protest Against Investors' Crazy
Consuming in Detroit

C hina has become again one of the world's major economic powers under the God of Wealth. The God of Wealth is in charge of commerce and directs the market since ancient times in China. In the decades following reform and capitalist opening-up in the late 1970s, China's economy has developed at a remarkable rate, with most of the growth created from Special Economic Zones (SEZ). The God of Wealth is very content with his achievement and has been eager to participate in a global game and deploy his "miracle" economic experiences across the world. In particular, he has been actively seeking opportunities to test out his power and strategy in the United States. The God of Wealth saw opportunities in the biggest municipal bankruptcy in U.S. history. Detroit was viewed as the Promised Land for Chinese manufacturing: it is strategically located on the Great Lakes, has low real estate prices in comparison with the rest of the USA, and most importantly carries the history and culture of industrialization; the Motor City was after all the Fordist test bed par excellence. With such vision, the God of Wealth spoke to the Minister of Commerce in dreams and provoked him about transforming Detroit into a special economic zone of China. The Minister found the suggestion very inspiring. Very soon, the Chinese government sent out a proposal entitled "Detroit S.A.R." to the city's emergency manager and the White House for Detroit to become an autonomous special economic zone. The official report highlighted the mutually beneficial nature of the agreement raising in particular the model of

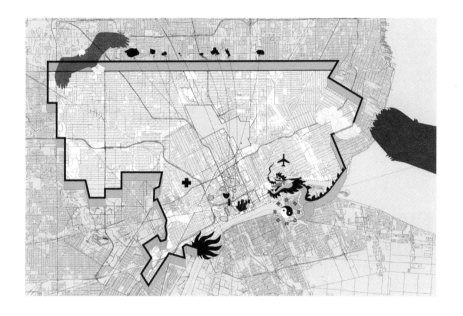

Hong Kong Special Administrative Region (Hong Kong S.A.R.). The evidence was undeniable and the agreement conclusive.

On July 1st, 2015, Detroit S.A.R. was established. By providing looser policies on visas, immigration, investment, and taxation, the government of Detroit S.A.R. wanted to attract wealthy investors from all over the world. The God of Wealth selected the best investors and opened them a door to the new city, Detroit S.A.R. Chinese manufacturing companies, which produce

goods for international brands such as Nike, Apple
and Coach, expanded their business overseas.
Detroit S.A.R. quickly overtook mainland China in
economic growth rates: the American Dragon was
born. The new administrative region reinvigorated
the local economy to fortunes never imagined. In
the meantime, investors brought radical changes
into the city. Lots of urban blocks are demolished
to give way for new real estate development.
Road signs were changed into bilingual with both
Chinese and English on them. Consumers from
China rushed into shopping malls to buy organic

food and luxury on sale. Kids were sent to local schools to prepare for college in the U.S. The God of Wealth was very satisfied that Detroit S.A.R. was the frontier of world capitalism.

Investors saw opportunities in sectors beyond the industry: the Detroit Institute of Arts, the Tiger Stadium and the Fox Theatre. They proposed to buy the art collection in the Detroit Institute of Arts, to change the Tiger Stadium into the Dragon Stadium, and the Fox Theatre into the Panda Theatre. The residents of Detroit's suburbs had mixed feelings toward the new fortunes of the city. Though they benefited from the newfound prosperity of their metro center, there arose a deep-seated fear of losing their cultural identity to these foreign investors, in particular the art collection of the Detroit Institute of Arts, the Tiger Stadium. In the eyes of local residents, the pandas showed little interest in the American Eagle. A protest against the plans of foreign investors took place on October 6th, 2023. Protesters requested that such important landmarks of the city be moved north of the city's 8 Mile Road administrative boundary. The tension between Chinese investors and local residents worried the God of Wealth. The God of Wealth decided to make some changes in the city to improve the situation. He researched human history, especially architectural history, looking for a solution. In the end, he realized a wall was what he needed to bring peace back to Detroit S.A.R. and surrounding cities.

In 2030, the landmarks were relocated. A border wall was built stretching the whole length of 8 Mile Road and wrapping around the city. To

The Great Wall
of Detroit S.A.R.

MALL

FACTORY

We provide a wide range of brands: luxurious, trendy and functional. The best-in-class shopping experience is tied to the manufacturing culture in Detroit S.A.R. Our on-site products are transported to the mall directly – we are never out of stock!

We offer the most efficient border crossing between the United States and China. The easy Homeland Security Subway allows you to cross the border on a daily basis. Just slide your passport or ID and run your bags through the security check machine, and you are through the Great Wall in 5 minutes!

Shopping

Border Crossing

WORKERS' DORMITORY

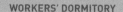

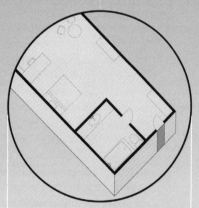

Ve proudly present our manufacturing ulture of Detroit S.A.R. The mysterious nass production scene is made ransparent and spectacular! Now hopping is not only buying, but lso learning what you buy. You are velcome to check out our advanced nanufacturing equipment and well-esigned working environment!

We take the well-being of our employee-family very seriously. We take seriously the issue of worker safety and understand that providing health care is very important. The worker not only survives but also thrives in In the Great Wall. Each employee is provided with their own dormitory room! Living next to the factory minimizes the time to commute. Common kitchens, laundry rooms, gyms and multi-function halls are provided to create an integrated worker's community.

Transparent Manufacturing

Worker-Friendly Environment

the north of the wall, the uprooted landmarks were connected to the wall as anchor stores. The Great Wall served to maintain the desired distance between Detroit S.A.R. and the suburbs, all while allowing both sides to share the glitter of the society of the spectacle. The Wall housed the mutual dreams – of American and Chinese capitalism together- for manufacturing and consumer society. Within the Wall were malls that also functioned as border crossings, factories and dormitories for local and overseas workers. The combination of these three units repeated the whole length of the Wall. The activities in the Wall were exposed to the public of the north suburbs as the image of a prospering Detroit S.A.R. The factories were "worker-friendly" environments for mass production. The Investment brochure* featured photo-essays on the Great Wall with great promises for the worker: "the dormitories are well-furnished and each employee has his/her own room! Our employee-family is well taken care of in both mental and physical health."

In Year 2036, Detroit SAR celebrated the Year of the Dragon with the sound of firecrackers. Along the 8 Mile Road, windows and doors were decorated with red paper-cuts of "good fortune" and "happiness". Money was given in red paper envelopes. The God of Wealth, in the form of a panda, was the new mascot of prosperity for Detroit S.A.R., the deity that was capable of turning its rubble and iron into gold.

CHAPTER 13

By Kevin (Pang-Hsin) Wang & Nicholas J. O'Leary

Tonight, I will end this life.
This is not the world I grew up in. A chess piece pinned on a two hundred square foot white box. Bounded. Absolute. Unrelenting walls inexorable after the hours I stare. Whispering a language without articulation, its only response the occasional pounding from the other side. A glimpse of life beyond these walls in the briefest of moments returns stoic as the door slams shut. Severed from desire, yearning of what is beyond reach. A barrier exists unseen and unnoticed. Few inches of air that separate its surface to me. I clean, I polish, I scrutinise over these encapsulating shells. They surround my life, yet recede into the background. There is no reason for contact. There is no reason to exist.

I am tired of these blank walls confining me. These lines are static. They are unforgiving. My English Ivy at the corner never made her reach to the window, she would not last the winter. Her shrivelled yellow leaves scattered on the floor mixed in with strands of my fallen hair, barely a foot away from salvation. Her remains will slowly decay along with the carcasses of the rats that rule this city; the shadows that inhabit a world between ours.

Inside. Outside. They are no longer any different. Over-sized openings show me another interior enclosing my own prison. The world out there. Another cage with more restrictions. More rules. More limits. More of the cold steel, and hard concrete walls. Endless, and anonymous. They grow taller every year; perhaps reaching for fresher air, perhaps searching for a spot further away from the rest. I see open windows beyond my own, they show me adjacent bodies remaining completely unaware of the next, longing for signs of life. I am no different from them. No more free. No more wiser. Each compartment dressed for escape. Paintings, photographs, elaborate sculptures, all reminders of places far from here. I was once an eagle, the Queen of my world. Now a battery chicken, a body without organs. Feeding this city.

Don't follow me. The unyielding pavement pounds against the bottom of my soles, vibrating the city up my spine. Don't follow me. The cold pierces through my skin and pricks at my bones. Don't follow me. The smell is nauseating, it lingers and reappears in my sleep. Don't follow me. The stench of rot and fading life penetrates the city, disguised by chemicals of ocean fresh, lavender blossoms, white linen. I am pursued by those I cannot see. Constant noise wherever I go. Sharp sirens and low horns. Bangs of the steam pipes. Creaks of the floorboards. Stilettos

against marble lobbies, and rattling of trains. A living corpse, this is the machine. This is the city.

I am disengaged with all that surrounds me. The footpath leads me to places I do not wish to go. This alienating city is bitter. Day after day I wake, I walk, I stand, and I sit. I am incarcerated within the flesh that has betrayed me. It takes me to spaces swarming with other lifeless forms, smashed inside a moving sardine can, transfixed to the sickly warm glow of the screen in their fat sticky fingers. Longing for connections in a virtual world. There is a thin film of slime on every surface. The metal bars smeared with fingerprints leave suggestions of previous life. Life, that is promised behind the posters. Life, that exists elsewhere. Vacant glances down to the ground, out of the darkened portholes partly obscured by the humid interior steaming up against the glass. Moist and stale. Suffocating. Occasional glimpses of flickering lights, and scribbles on surfaces defiant of the city. Still, there is no escape.

Where can I go? The city rejects me. Pounding lights and deafening sound, mixed in with smells of alcohol, smoke, and sweat, find me no refuse. Flocks of a new religion, looking for machines of freedom. Dripping bodies grinding against the next faceless form provide no more connection than my lifeless walls. It numbs whatever was left at the end of the day. Accepted obscenity in a neat box, with a cherry on top.

My body aches, movements prescribed. The city is the architect of my body, the puppeteer with invisible strings. It tells me where to walk, where to stand, and where to sit. I am judged wherever I go. Eyes from behind the curtains, above the newspapers and dirty magazines. They see me, they judge me, and they haunt my every move. See what good little girls and boys are made of. We stand in coloured lines, moving one step at a time motioned by flashing numbers overhead. The factory floor of the human farm. Order inscribed into our psyche is not without constant reminders. Signs and lights burn into my eyes wherever I look. They say,

No Standing Anytime.

No Climbing.

No Sitting.

Keep Off, Private.

Green.

Orange.

Red.

Stop.

Every inch of this city screams at me.

No more.

No more attachments with this city, nothing would remain. I will not be missed, a headline soon forgotten. They called me crazy when I was younger. Last time I fell there was more. A world that moved me. A world with life. A wonderland created for the girl I was then. Now stuck in this moment that I've been told as truth, constructed with glittering gold. No more wandering blind. I have to get back.

I will fall. I will succumb to the city. Return to the blank slate, and we will be bound together in flesh and mind.

Eternally,

Alice L. Dodgson

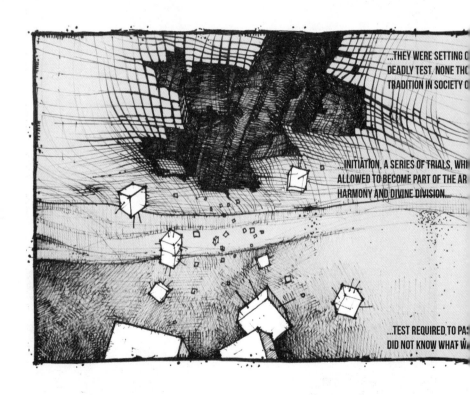

...THEY WERE SETTING C
DEADLY TEST. NONE THC
TRADITION IN SOCIETY C

...INITIATION, A SERIES OF TRIALS, WHI
ALLOWED TO BECOME PART OF THE AR
HARMONY AND DIVINE DIVISION...

...TEST REQUIRED TO PA:
DID NOT KNOW WHAT W.

HYPNAGOGIC SET OF EVENTS EXPERIENCED BY 132X12866Y78Z

By Zygmunt Maniaczyk & Marcin Kitala

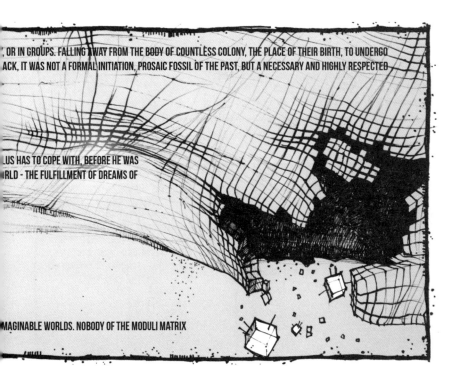

, OR IN GROUPS. FALLING AWAY FROM THE BODY OF COUNTLESS COLONY, THE PLACE OF THEIR BIRTH, TO UNDERGO
ACK, IT WAS NOT A FORMAL INITIATION, PROSAIC FOSSIL OF THE PAST, BUT A NECESSARY AND HIGHLY RESPECTED

LUS HAS TO COPE WITH, BEFORE HE WAS
RLD - THE FULFILLMENT OF DREAMS OF

MAGINABLE WORLDS. NOBODY OF THE MODULI MATRIX

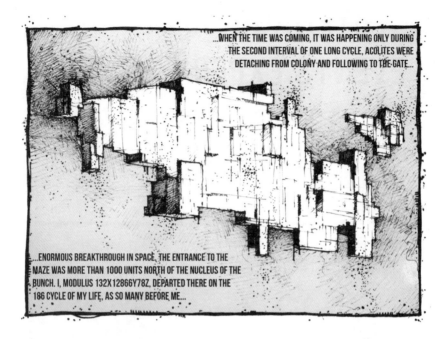

...WHEN THE TIME WAS COMING, IT WAS HAPPENING ONLY DURING THE SECOND INTERVAL OF ONE LONG CYCLE, ACOLITES WERE DETACHING FROM COLONY AND FOLLOWING TO THE GATE...

...ENORMOUS BREAKTHROUGH IN SPACE. THE ENTRANCE TO THE MAZE WAS MORE THAN 1000 UNITS NORTH OF THE NUCLEUS OF THE BUNCH. I, MODULUS 132X12866Y78Z, DEPARTED THERE ON THE 186 CYCLE OF MY LIFE, AS SO MANY BEFORE ME...

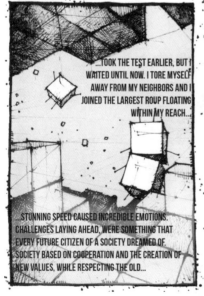

...TOOK THE TEST EARLIER, BUT I WAITED UNTIL NOW. I TORE MYSELF AWAY FROM MY NEIGHBORS AND I JOINED THE LARGEST ROUP FLOATING WITHIN MY REACH...

...STUNNING SPEED CAUSED INCREDIBLE EMOTIONS. CHALLENGES LAYING AHEAD, WERE SOMETHING THAT EVERY FUTURE CITIZEN OF A SOCIETY DREAMED OF. SOCIETY BASED ON COOPERATION AND THE CREATION OF NEW VALUES, WHILE RESPECTING THE OLD...

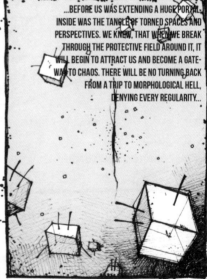

...BEFORE US WAS EXTENDING A HUGE PORTAL. INSIDE WAS THE TANGLE OF TORNED SPACES AND PERSPECTIVES. WE KNEW, THAT WHEN WE BREAK THROUGH THE PROTECTIVE FIELD AROUND IT, IT WILL BEGIN TO ATTRACT US AND BECOME A GATE-WAY TO CHAOS. THERE WILL BE NO TURNING BACK FROM A TRIP TO MORPHOLOGICAL HELL, DENYING EVERY REGULARITY...

...WE FIND OURSELVES IN FRONT OF THE MOUTH OF THE DEAD GOD...

UNDERSTOOD THAT MANY WILL NOT BE ABLE TO GET TO THE OTHER SIDE...

... FIRST VICTIMS...

...VESTIBULE OF FAITH...

...SLOWLY, ONE BY ONE, MY COMPANIONS SUBMERGED INTO THE DARKNESS THAT SEEMED TO ADVANCED FROM ALL SIDES...

...SUDDENLY THE GATE CLOSED BEHIND US AND I FELT THAT I BEGIN TO ROTATE IN THE HUGE VORTEX... CENTRIFUGAL FORCE WAS TO STRONG... COLLLIED WITH A GROUP OF MY BROTHERS... STILL ACCELERATING...

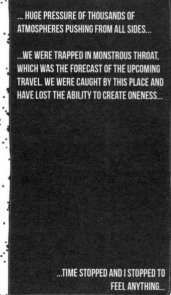

... HUGE PRESSURE OF THOUSANDS OF ATMOSPHERES PUSHING FROM ALL SIDES...

...WE WERE TRAPPED IN MONSTROUS THROAT, WHICH WAS THE FORECAST OF THE UPCOMING TRAVEL. WE WERE CAUGHT BY THIS PLACE AND HAVE LOST THE ABILITY TO CREATE ONENESS...

...TIME STOPPED AND I STOPPED TO FEEL ANYTHING...

...VAST PLAIN...

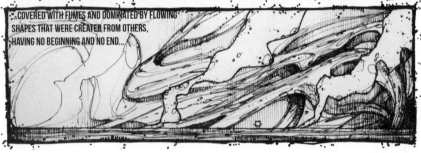

...COVERED WITH FUMES AND DOMINATED BY FLOWING SHAPES THAT WERE CREATED FROM OTHERS, HAVING NO BEGINNING AND NO END...

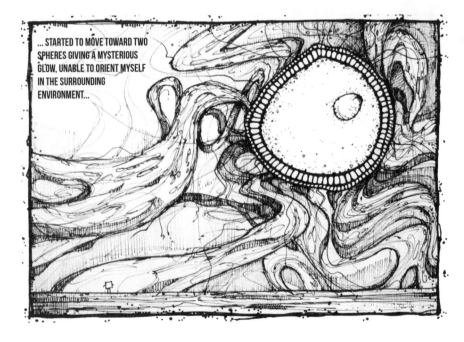

... STARTED TO MOVE TOWARD TWO SPHERES GIVING A MYSTERIOUS GLOW, UNABLE TO ORIENT MYSELF IN THE SURROUNDING ENVIRONMENT...

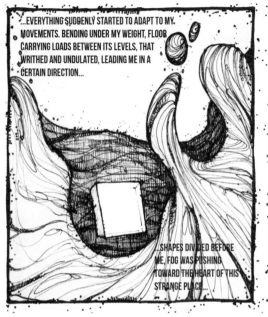

...EVERYTHING SUDDENLY STARTED TO ADAPT TO MY MOVEMENTS. BENDING UNDER MY WEIGHT, FLOOR CARRYING LOADS BETWEEN ITS LEVELS, THAT WRITHED AND UNDULATED, LEADING ME IN A CERTAIN DIRECTION...

...SHAPES DIVIDED BEFORE ME, FOG WAS PUSHING TOWARD THE HEART OF THIS STRANGE PLACE...

...SMALL CREATURES RUNNING SOMEWHERE ON THE BORDER OF SIGHT, BUT NEVER CAME OUT FROM THE SHADOWS...

...SOMETHING BEGAN TO CHANGE...

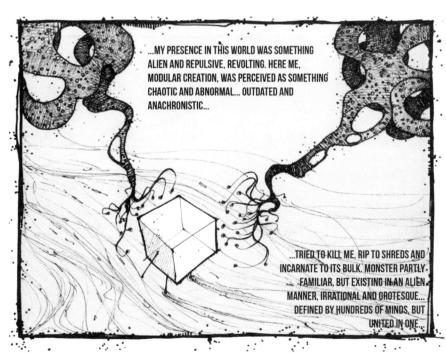

...MY PRESENCE IN THIS WORLD WAS SOMETHING ALIEN AND REPULSIVE, REVOLTING. HERE ME, MODULAR CREATION, WAS PERCEIVED AS SOMETHING CHAOTIC AND ABNORMAL... OUTDATED AND ANACHRONISTIC...

...TRIED TO KILL ME, RIP TO SHREDS AND INCARNATE TO ITS BULK. MONSTER PARTLY FAMILIAR, BUT EXISTING IN AN ALIEN MANNER, IRRATIONAL AND GROTESQUE... DEFINED BY HUNDREDS OF MINDS, BUT UNITED IN ONE...

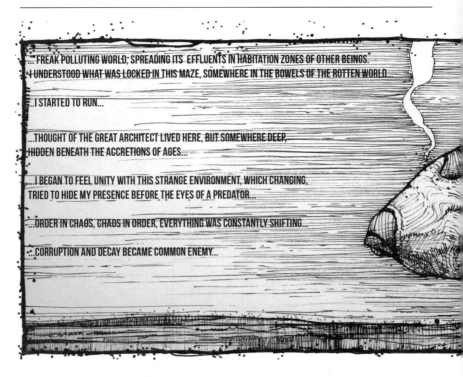

...FREAK POLLUTING WORLD; SPREADING ITS EFFLUENTS IN HABITATION ZONES OF OTHER BEINGS.
I UNDERSTOOD WHAT WAS LOCKED IN THIS MAZE, SOMEWHERE IN THE BOWELS OF THE ROTTEN WORLD...

...I STARTED TO RUN...

...THOUGHT OF THE GREAT ARCHITECT LIVED HERE, BUT SOMEWHERE DEEP,
HIDDEN BENEATH THE ACCRETIONS OF AGES...

...I BEGAN TO FEEL UNITY WITH THIS STRANGE ENVIRONMENT, WHICH CHANGING,
TRIED TO HIDE MY PRESENCE BEFORE THE EYES OF A PREDATOR...

...ORDER IN CHAOS, CHAOS IN ORDER, EVERYTHING WAS CONSTANTLY SHIFTING...

...CORRUPTION AND DECAY BECAME COMMON ENEMY...

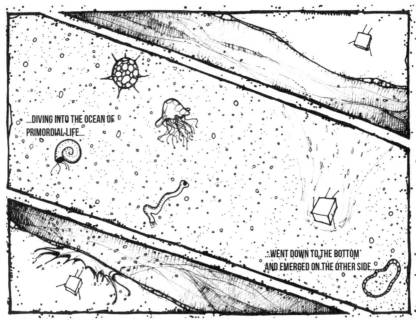

...DIVING INTO THE OCEAN OF
PRIMORDIAL LIFE...

...WENT DOWN TO THE BOTTOM
AND EMERGED ON THE OTHER SIDE...

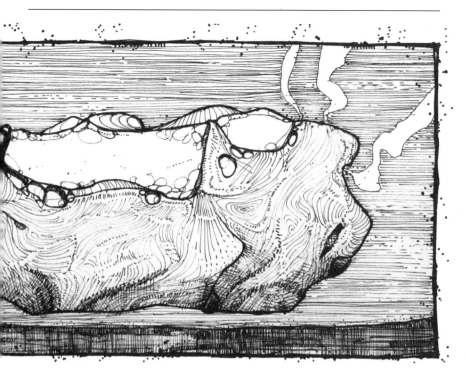

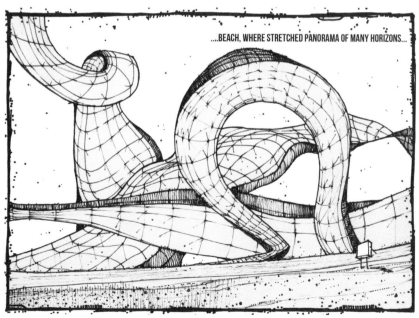

...BEACH, WHERE STRETCHED PANORAMA OF MANY HORIZONS...

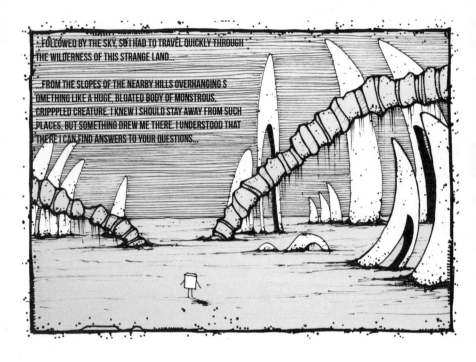

...HIGHER AND HIGHER, APPROACHING SKELETON OF THE LEVIATHAN, COATED WITH REMAINS OF ONCE-LIVING MATTER...

...WANDERING THROUGH THE BELLY OF A GIANT, I REALIZED THAT IT IS BUILD OF MILLIONS OF SMALL CREATURES JUST LIKE OUR COLONY. ONE BODY WITH MANY CELLS...

...ONE WAS STILL ALIVE. TO MY SURPRISE, IT STARTED TO MOVE AND ATTACK ITS DEAD NEIGHBORS. AFTER A WHILE, EXHAUSTED, IT STOPPED MOVING AND COLLAPSED INTO DUST. I REALIZED THAT THIS WAS THE CAUSE OF DEATH OF THIS SO PERFECT, COMPLEX BODY.

THE ARROGANCE TOWARD THOSE WITH WHOM WE FORM ONE. THE FALSE BELIEF THAT YOU BELONG ONLY TO YOURSELF. NOT PAYING ATTENTION TO THOSE, WITH WHICH WE ARE CONNECTED...

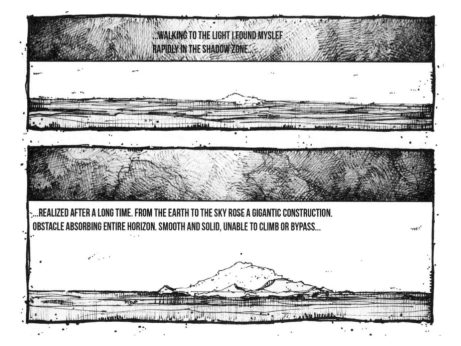

...WALKING TO THE LIGHT I FOUND MYSLEF RAPIDLY IN THE SHADOW ZONE...

...REALIZED AFTER A LONG TIME. FROM THE EARTH TO THE SKY ROSE A GIGANTIC CONSTRUCTION. OBSTACLE ABSORBING ENTIRE HORIZON. SMOOTH AND SOLID, UNABLE TO CLIMB OR BYPASS...

...BARROW, BUILD FROM THE BODIES OF MY DEAD BROTHERS, MODULI. ABOVE, IN THE WALL THE WAS A SINGLE HOLE, A PASSAGE...

...ROUND AND TOO SMALL FOR NORMAL MODULUS TO FIT. I REALIZED THE REASON FOR THEIR FAILURE...

...WHAT TO DO? HOW TO GET TO THE OTHER SIDE? IT CANNOT HAPPEN, NOT TO ME!

...I CLIMBED UP THE BODIES OF THOSE WHO CAME BEFORE ME. I SAW MYSELF IN THEM, GUIDED THROUGH ALL THE TROUBLES BY THE PROMISE OF BELONGING TO THE ELECTED, THOSE WHO COULD MAKE CHANGES...

...WHAT TO DO...

...WHAT...

...I KNOW!

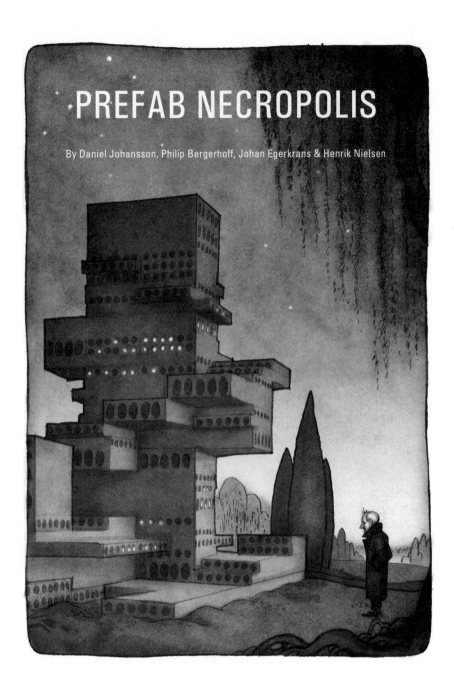

This is the story about the prefab necropolis in the outskirts of the northern city. It is a peculiar architectural project that has evoked interest in many ways since the heartbroken architect who created it was the first one to be buried in the depth of the prefabricated concrete elements.

Some looked upon the tower-like concrete structures that composed this city of the dead with disgust, referring to its creator as an ego-centric lout. Others called the project a wonder of the world and anxiously signed the contract that guaranteed a "hole" in the necropolis when life came to an end.

After the first urn had been placed in the first little carriage and rolled into one of the five canals in the first concrete element, many thought that it marked the beginning and the end of the project and that the huge piece of land obtained by this so called architect would soon be bought back by the city and used for more relevant and rational purposes.

But the first urn did not become the last. Not long after the death of the architect another person surprisingly decided to spend their eternal rest within the confinements of the necropolis. The contract signed by the second inhabitant not only guaranteed an urn and a canal to put it in. To everyone's surprise it also held the obligation to donate at least one point two meters of con-crete element by the height of either 200 or 400 millimeters. This meant that for every person who was buried, at least five new canals of eternal rest were generated for the necropolis. And those who

'wished for a spot but could not afford the donation
would get one of the remaining four channels of
each element. But most could afford it. You see,
one of the unique features of the elements was
that they were being produced in great amounts
and therefore were rather cheap compared to the
alternatives offered by traditional burials in one of
the town's cemeteries. The factory that produced
the elements for housing projects first thought
it was a joke, but as time passed the deliveries
to the necropolis started to grow and as always
the money involved was more seductive than the
skeptical voices. Some thought that the very nature
of the rational elements were in danger when used
for such unquantifiable purposes. What was the
purpose anyway? No one was sure, but everyone in
town seemed to have their own idea about it.

    Many claimed that the architect had despised
the simplification that architectural practice had
become, and that the complexities that used to be
a part of building had been infested by a language
based on simple, market driven terms of quantifi-
able measures and blunt ideals.

    He had worked most of his life for one of the
bigger firms in town and was known as a good

craftsman who would fiddle with physical model making when the more linear minded had moved on along the graph.

The bigger the necropolis became the more rumors about the purposes seemed to emerge. As speculations hit the streets more and more people wanted to be a part of the structure and more and more signed the contract. There was even hearsay of suicides generated by the architecture in order for the structure to grow even faster. You see, nobody knew how vast the city would be when it was finished, or if there even was an end. There was a janitor, a relative of the architect, who was in charge of maintaining the structure. Every time he held the drawings someone peaked over his shoulder to get a closer look at the instructions. There were a few simple rules. One was the use of a grid that was 1.2x1.2 meters. Another was the way that the elements were stacked. The top

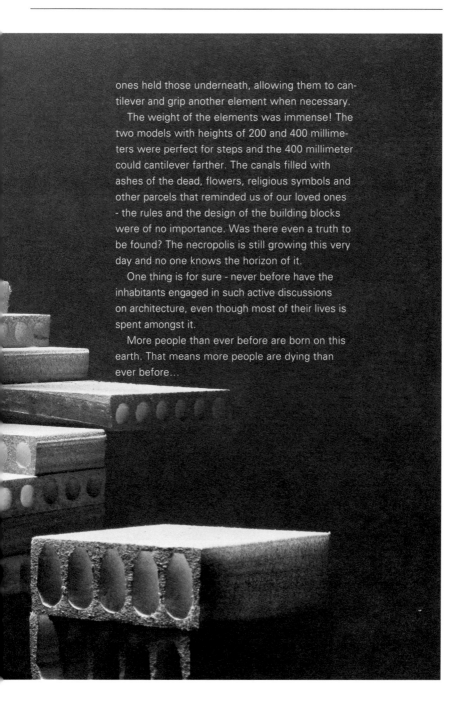

ones held those underneath, allowing them to cantilever and grip another element when necessary.

The weight of the elements was immense! The two models with heights of 200 and 400 millimeters were perfect for steps and the 400 millimeter could cantilever farther. The canals filled with ashes of the dead, flowers, religious symbols and other parcels that reminded us of our loved ones - the rules and the design of the building blocks were of no importance. Was there even a truth to be found? The necropolis is still growing this very day and no one knows the horizon of it.

One thing is for sure - never before have the inhabitants engaged in such active discussions on architecture, even though most of their lives is spent amongst it.

More people than ever before are born on this earth. That means more people are dying than ever before...

OCULARCENTRISM

By Gianna Papapavlou

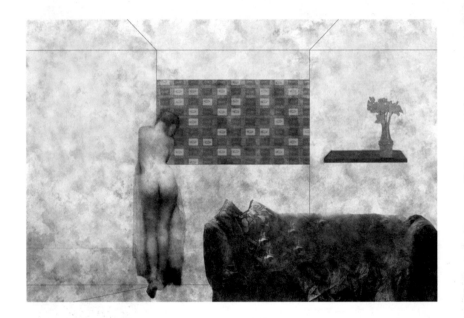

S he used to sit alone for hours gazing out the window. The view was from the condominium across the street. A building identical to the one she was living in. These twin buildings were facing and mirroring each other.

The window frame enclosed a small area of the endless façade of the building. Its façade gave the impression of a flat piece of paper with countless orthonormal rectangular holes. Lacking in depth, almost shallow, this enormous wall left only to imagination what could be happening behind it.

Something that was unknown.

The only proof of life inside the opposite building was through the opening and closing of the windows. The façade was "blinking" in a specific rhythm throughout the day. This sole exertion indicated life within, and so she was filled with optimism that her only way out to the outside world was not so empty and shallow but indeed a vessel of life.

She enjoyed observing the temporal change of the façade. It was an amusing game to her. More like a playful interaction between her and the life within the opposite building. She perceived the façade as an enormous grid for noughts and crosses, and so the open windows were altered to noughts, while the closed ones to crosses.

So this was the way she was living and so this was the way she felt that others were living as well. It was her and the rest of the world. Carnal entities with their existence based in reciprocity where they can be reversed and intertwined with each other. Corporeal beings constituted of general visibility and bodily reflexivity, therefore the ability to see meant to be seen in reverse.

These were the thoughts that occupied her mind and she started to feel that there must have been a reversed gaze behind all of those windows across hers. By standing behind an open window she kept feeling watched by someone whose eyes she had never seen. In this position she felt she was being altered into an object for vision, to be seen and perceived by the others that lived inside the opposite building.

The two buildings were identical mirrored vessels of life, but the buildings themselves were soulless constructions, empty nets that in order to be filled had to hold the souls of their residents. They were not merely buildings, but rather a collection of human souls, therefore a cage where everyone was kept captive. Their only way out was through the regions that were not filled, the spaces enclosed by the window openings.

By being frontal and mirrored, the windows of the two buildings became themselves mirrors as what they reflected were self-portraits projected to the outside world. And this is how she saw him. These two entities were a mirror for each other and functioned existentially as objects to be

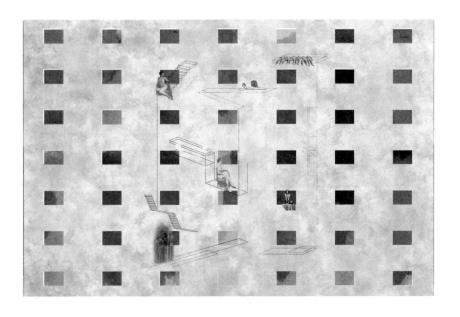

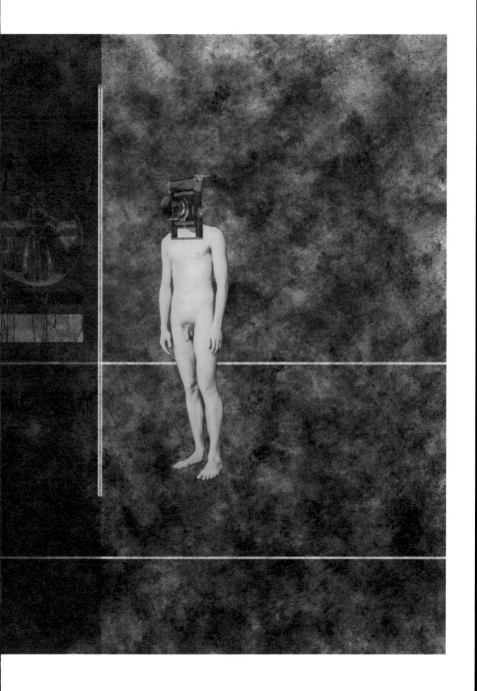

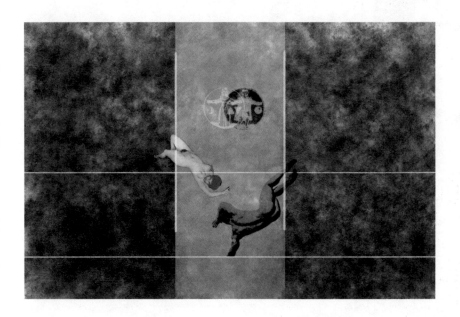

seen as well as subjects that can see.

He, looking inside the frame of her window, was so fascinated by the notion of capturing her. Enclosed by frames and cut out from the total experience of vision she became a target. His eyes were functioning like guns, targeting the excised by the window frame, piece of her whole entity.

He captured her by the complete absorption of her otherness and the simultaneous injection of his individuality into her. He projected himself into her and by liking what he was seeing, his own reflection, he reached to grab and kiss her.

But the more he was reaching and the closer he was getting to her, he felt more and more repelled by his "creation". He transformed her into an empty vessel in which he blew into all the smoke and ugliness of his own soul. She ceased to be beautiful, because she ceased to be someone else and she became him.

His hopeless attempt to reach her and get near her did not prosper. He stumbled and fell and dragged her with him. They fell on the ground, the interspace of their buildings and their gazes. And there they lay in this habitable space consisted of temporality, motion, interaction and hapticness. In this position, they were finally able to see in one another the wholeness and the otherness.

That was the time he realized the callousness of his actions and he exclaimed:

"This is our place. This is where we should stay. The interval of these two rigid thresholds is our home. This street is our dwelling and it's perfect! The sky is the roof, while the stars and the sun are the lightings. The facades of the buildings are the walls of our compartment. Lastly, the open windows are the cornices of interchangeable self-portraits of the rest of the members of our family."

"Now, in this position, I can see you and I can see both of us clearly."

EXORDIUM

By Posin Wang

E xordium, the beginning. Exordium is a reality where free floating planes exhibit their own artificial gravity, thereby negating a universal ground plane. This technology allows for multi-surface occupation and a shift in how we perceive directionality and basic spatial orientation. In this society, occupants go about their daily lives in a fleeting world, where space and time are intertwined - that is, space becomes temporal and time becomes spatial.

Space becomes temporal due to the random and spontaneous reconfigurations of these floating pieces. The way in which they come together helps to break up spaces, intersect events, and provide a constant state of suspense to the occupants as to what will come next. No one knows where they will wake up today, how they will go to work or how they will come home. Or better yet, what then becomes home? These occupants might have ownership of a single planar surface, but the constantly changing adjoining pieces only temporarily come together to form an enclosure. Home is an idea rather than a spatial constant.

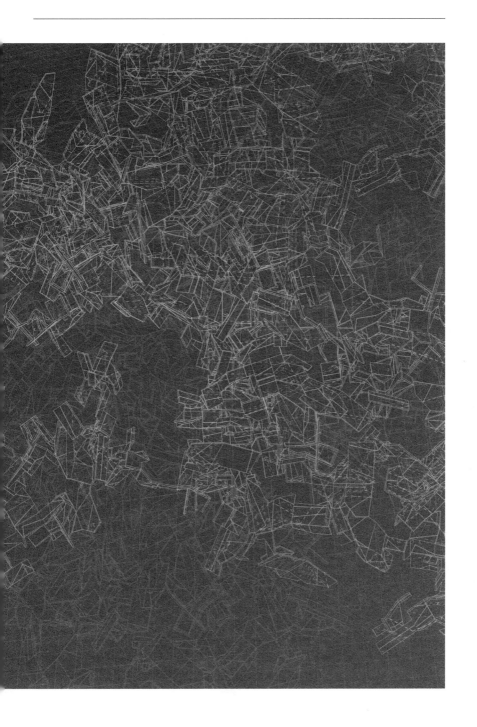

Time becomes spatial in this world. As the planes are constantly shifting, each and every event that takes place receives its own unique spatial manifestation. For example, if a blue, red and yellow plane come together in a certain configuration when someone's girlfriend decides to break up with them, that painful experience becomes linked to that specific blue, red and yellow space.

This is a configuration of three individual "pieces," having temporarily joined to form unique spatial relationships. The section cut depicts the structural and technical inner-workings of these pieces. It also shows the various topological variations within each surface. Each plane must be able to function in any orientation. Without this ability, enclosure would become extinct, and meaningful spatial relationships would disappear.

Our story begins in the Nisop Industrial District, where a supposedly "mad prophet" begins to question the nature of his reality. He is disillusioned with the world around him, he so begins his preaching against the so-called visionaries who created it. These architects of reality presented a world in which spatial experiences have infinite possibilities. They utilized artificial gravity as a means to achieve a habitable reality of organized chaos. The unceasing shifting of these pieces allows for unpredictable, and ultimately unrepeatable, configurations of spaces. This dynamic system keeps inhabitants aware of, and constantly engaged in, their environment. Occupants are constantly connected to one another; there is always a path from one piece to another.

To the nameless wandering vagrant of our story, the benevolence of this world's creators is questionable - it "doesn't feel right." He attempts

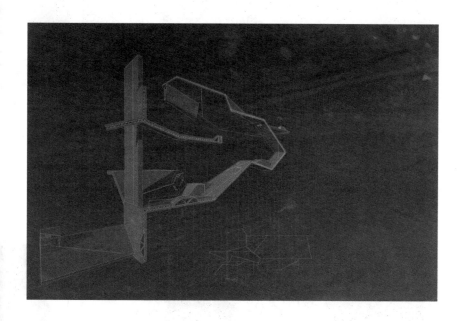

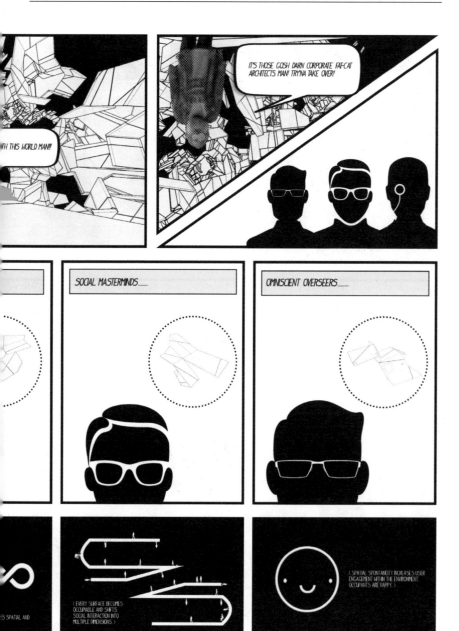

to share his "revelations" to the passing crowd, but is ignored and deemed mentally unstable. He says the world is confusing, lacking orientation and is ultimately a trap set by the ruling visionaries to secretly retain control of the world. Why else would this world have no way out? It seems to continue forever in every direction and just when you think you have reached an edge, more pieces float forth to meet you. It may appear as an open, unending circulatory system, but in reality is simply an ingenious prison (or so our prophet might have you believe). He assumes that there are possible spatial restraints to this world, but these restraints are being kept secret. Is there really a finite edge in this reality? Is there another place to go?

He then questions how these seemingly "random" pieces really move around. He believes that the pieces are configured to move for a darker unknown purpose. It is however possible, that these pieces really do rotate and freely navigate in zero gravity until they are within proximity of another attracting force. As he continues to rant, suddenly, whether purposeful or not, a floating piece comes crashing down in front of the prophet. He is surprised. A plane from the farming sector has wandered into his vicinity bringing along a friendly lost cow. It seems as though the prophet has finally found a willing audience. By the end of the story, it is unclear whether our anti-hero and his newly found bovine ally are indeed enlightened souls, or simply misguided creatures living in a perfect world.

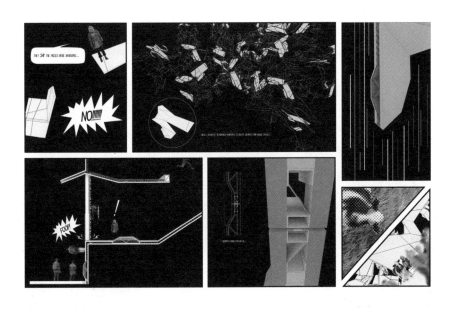

THE EXTRAVAGANT JOURNEY OF MR. BLUE

By Gladys Cheung, Lisa Sato & Elizabeth Belina-Brzozowski

SCENE 1

Once upon a time, Mr. Beul sits on his ordinary chair, within his ordinary cubicle, staring out into the ordinary distance. Surrounded by three suffocating walls; boredom strikes. An overwhelming feeling of emptiness has penetrated him and there is no way out. He wants something new in his life. Something exciting. Something different.

The clock roars as the seconds slowly creep to their next destination.

"HAZAH! I am free!" They have set him free from the confines of his cube. He packs up his things, sways his hat over his head and flees. But what Mr. Beul does not know is that he is running towards another empty hole; the city. As he slowly drags his feet towards home he notices other pale fellow citizens like himself. No smiles, no eye contact; a mass of dragging rags. Dragging their bodies forward, one lifeless step after the next, towards home to their dreary couch, to watch their dreary television, and to stare off into the dreary distance before awakening to a dreary cubicle. He looks up at the skyscrapers around him to distract him from negative thoughts but can't help but find empty white walls and glaring reflective windows lined up in infinite order. "How can these building host anything remotely interesting...It is obvious they exist to put us to work and cage us from normality" He wondered numbingly.

He halts. Shakes his head. Frustrated with the
banality of his reality, Mr. Beul storms off to find
himself a nice restaurant to gather his thoughts,
as hunger beckons his appetite.

SCENE 2

Mr. Beul walks and walks the asphalt sidewalks
of Dull City but little did he know that this was
not the ordinary city that was once his home. He
eventually walks past an alleyway where he spots
a restaurant hidden alone in a courtyard. Curious -
he walks deeper into the dark alleyway to find dark
mysterious creatures dumping wastes into funnels
that sit atop the glowing five-star restaurant.
Very intrigued by this seemingly extravagant
place he walks closer to the wooden door. Above
the awning a Chef appears waving to his new
customer and announces to Mr. Beul: "Welcome!
Your table awaits!"

Mr. Beul surprised by the warm welcome,
waves back only to find he has strangely changed
to a curious shade of blue. About to panic, a dozen
waiters with long mustaches barge through the
door, pick up Mr. Blue, and drag him inside to his
table while singing:

"What a wonderful time to
join us, join us, join us!
Infinite menus and endless fun
Unlimited cupcakes and loads of buns
Pizza and bacon, there is no order
Ice-creams and chocolates, simple disorder
What a wonderful time to join us,
join us, join us!"

Mr. Blue, now transformed and entertained
by these wonderful waiters, becomes even
more enthralled by this fantastical restaurant as
he looks up to its ceiling. The orange funnels
that he spots puncture through the ceiling and
pump out lines of junk food that only the most
voracious will attempt. Bacon ice-cream sundaes,
cronuts, pepperoni cinnabons. One by one, they
appear onto a floating moving conveyor belt that
delivers processed food straight into the patrons'
mouths, while they sit back and devour their

meals. Confused but eager to try, the conveyor belt wraps around Mr. Blue and pushes the indulgences into his throat. Not sure when the fun will end, he devours and devours until his body becomes transformed into an animal of gluttony - a pig. He eventually falls over onto the ground where the room begins to spin. His heart aches. He reaches a state of coma while the restaurant slowly fades around him.

SCENE 3

Mr. Blue wakes up stripped of clothes and disoriented by the emptiness around him. After his gluttonous adventure, he craves more stimulation. As if responding to his call for excitement a magic carpet appears with vein-like tentacles. Surprised, he holds on tight as the carpet takes off to drop him in front of a hotel. Sure that the last event was a strange dream he finds himself staring at the hotel convinced that something seems off about it. The building seems rather wide at the top and changes in size and direction as he approaches it.

Hoping to return to his normal skin color after a good rest, he enters the hotel finding it rather empty. "Hello?! ...echo...He notices the walls and ceiling are covered in red velvet carpet and there is a hole carved out of the center of the room. He walks closer to the hole and suddenly a large fish pops up from the bottom swallowing him whole. It reopens its mouth wide to lightly blow a floating bubble with Mr. Blue and a strange Miss sitting by his side. He notices her long hair, her beautiful exposed breasts and her scaled tail. "A mermaid?" he wonders. Unexpectedly, a massive slimy tongue thrashes through the window and reaches under the bubble to eject them upwards toward the ceiling. He looks at her confused. She begins to tickle his ankles with her tail enticing him to kneel next to her. They begin to kiss and forget to notice that their bodies are becoming larger and larger as they float higher and higher.

The hotel begins to expand around the waist of the bubble morphing into a sphere. The outer concrete of the walls begin to burst as the two lay on top on each other.

The building extends to clouds above with lovers wrapped around each other. Suddenly the ceiling begins to crack eventually bursting through the ceiling freeing them from enclosure. He's thrusting and she's breathing heavily singing:

"Darling Blueeeeeeee!
Let us hover over the city
Where we can bloom
Over something pretty
Darling Blueeeeeeee!
Feeling freedom of our souls
Without traps and holes
To stop us from our bores
Darling Blueeeeeee!

SCENE 4

The mermaid's voice echoes and she asks him for more. He begins to stare off to the distance as he feels empty inside, finding himself bored of the situation once more. He realizes that it was neither lust nor gluttony he was looking for and attempts to fill his void once more. He ponders what to do next and asks himself: "If it isn't physical pleasure that can erase this boredom, perhaps I can alter my mental state and escape reality." He suddenly remembers that there was a hospital with a psychiatric ward nearby that was known to distribute low dosage pain-killers to the

public. The bubble floats and bobs and finally pops in front of a hospital that seems indefinably odd.

He enters into a strange looking corridor spotting a posse of seemingly helpful nurses. The interior was covered in colorful brains that moved like a screen saver side to side bumping into each other. Dazed, Mr. Blue tries to regain focus and introduces himself. He explains his excruciating pain and void but the nurses turn to him and in a synchronized voice tone as him "Would you like morphine clowns or codeine stars?" Nervously, Mr. Blue accepted the morphine. The nurses smiled and all together pricked him with giant multicolored needles as he fell into a new place, a different place, something more...

The nurses began to float away from his point of view while a door opened up to him revealing a room where the walls started to close in on him and crystallize. The room became distorted and he was unable to tell what reality was and what was not. A large mouth appeared and started to spew pills and needles in his direction. Operating tables turned into habitable tents while gowned animals danced in circles singing: "La la la lou, la la la bloo, la la la blue". Sweaty, Mr. Blue reaches for a hospital bed in the corner hoping to escape the madness. He begins to scream to himself: "I don't want anymore! More is trouble. More is tiresome. More is distraction. Let us celebrate 'mores' funeral for it must end!" The room continues to spin.

SCENE 5

"I am Mr. Beul...and I want nothing more and nothing less..." He cries. The room slowly stops spinning. The crowd slowly disappears into the cracked walls. The nurses melt into the floor. And once again, upon a time, Mr. Beul is laying in his hospital bed resting in the comfort of his four walls.

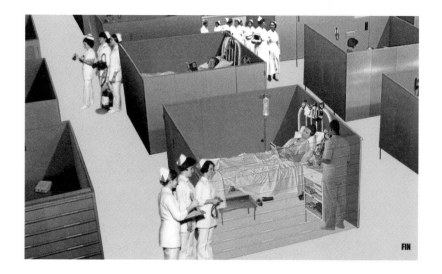

NARRATOR

And so let us snooze and hibernate for
winter or fall to re-evaluate what distractions
us citizens wish for. We may find ourselves in
an overindulged city where madness meets us
around the corner singing songs of surrealist
binges and disorder. Let our buildings sing with
lyrical components that make us smile. Let them
have magnetic forces to catch our gaze without
drowning our values. Let our city speak to us to
continue the conversation we began. For escape
from banality may not be a demanding request but
rather a physical burden we will not bare to the
grave.

SYNESTHESIA: THE AQUAPHILIC NOMAD

By Henry Cheung

Towards a Hyperspecific Architecture

Homogeneity in architecture prohibits the evolution of architecture. It provides an endless stale-platform of sameness. Individuals are different and therefore, architecture should be different. Synesthesia operates through hyper-specificity – accounting for fine adaptation and personal idiosyncrasies while incorporating a light sense of daily absurdities.

Architecture is too general, often producing moments of submission within a highly choreographed standardized realm. The generality of architecture stems from mass adaptation and production – yielding standards in space, movement, and mind while stifling hyper-specific personal idiosyncrasies. Generality masks the quirks, the eccentricities, and oddities of life – of mundane daily occurrences and micro-infatuations. It exposes architecture as a purist, a fixer-upper, and an advocate of homogeneity.

3:00 am / the awakening / home

wakes up and brushes / 20
mins. uses the bathroom / 15
mins. washes face / 10 mins.
grabs backpack and departs /
2 mins.

nomad's path

0   2   4   8 ft

5.30 am / the weave / net store

enters and walks towards the
large nylon net + browses /
20 mins. purchases new net
for fishing / 5 mins. departs
for the bladder boat.

0   2   4   8 ft

My protagonist, the aquaphilic nomad in Long Beach California, navigates through space based on his/her daily narrative while indulging in his/her personal idiosyncrasies. Idiosyncrasies expel normalcy while heightening the relationship between the built and specific assemblages. The project proposes to reconfigure banality into hyper-specific space. Architecture should not hinder the protagonist's choreographed paths; rather it should heighten and amplify his/her experiential absurdities and involuntary daily sensations.

The waves of the Pacific hits the earlier-riser, drenching his salt-crusted hair and lightly groomed eyebrows. He flings backwards, gripping onto his saturated cotton net – hoping for an abundant catch. The boat wanders and tilts – dancing independently in the glimmering moonlight as the waves trough and crest. The morning dew sets in as the sun begins to peak above the horizon. Shadows ripple across the blanketed-ocean. It glistens as the aquaphilic nomad continues to haul, pull, and ponder about his daily catchment. His provision depends on his sales at the San Pedro fish market. A splash in the distance diverts his attention while his net continues to work. A vicious drag propels the fatigued boat forward, and the cotton net begins to fill – choking the catchment in its place. The nomad grins and titters – nervously awaiting the pull.

He heaves as the net migrates to the bow – chipping away at the tattered panels. His catchment spills into the boat – five, ten, twenty, thirty, forty – he counts. The morning fog sets in

6:00 am / the hunt / bladder fishing boat

travels to fishing site / 15
mins. fishes / 2 hrs. cleans
and preps fish for birdcage
coffeehouse / 1 hr.

0   2   4   8 ft

salt water environment

sandy mud environment

walnut

opaque ETFE

hand painted upholstery

neoprene bed

chrysanthemum printed vinyl

herringbone counter

oxblood leather

espresso scented atmosphere

pioneer ddj-xs dj controller set

la marzocco linea 2 mechanical paddle espresso machine

as the engine murmurs back to the sun-kissed sand – reminiscent of speckled glass broken by a drunken hoot. He sells his catch at the daily fish market and stashes several large trout in his ice chest for supper. He returns to his temporary RV as the hand moves to seven. He slips into his damp wetsuit, clenches his surfboard, and manages to grab a handful of raw almonds as he lunges for the door. The weary nomad sprints, gripping his toes to the sand – collecting company along the way. His earlier routine escapes his mind. He focuses on one task and one task only – to conquer the daily challenge of the Pacific. He leaps as his feet breaks the icy shore. His body molds to the board as he paddles toward the horizon. The aquaphilic nomad rides and carves with grace as his body mimics the concave waves. The sun splits to eleven as his body gives. The soreness and hunger set in and is reminded of his two o'clock awakening. He respires and carries on.

He lives to carve, to conquer, and be challenge. Although he lives a nomadic lifestyle, he ceases to stray far from the aqua.

Possessions are a minimum for the aquaphilic nomad. He is equipped with a mustard aluminum teardrop trailer, a surfboard, a tattered fishing boat, large cotton net, white-tees, and a bag of wax.

THE NEW ARRANGEMENT

By Sarah Vaz

Two irreconcilable desires compete: we need novelty, yet we wish to survive. Once, novelty meant survival. Invention and ingenuity made us the most adaptable of species. We flourished, and then we sprawled. Few obstructions remained to our continued inhabitation of the planet, but the impulse to innovate, to produce, and to build was too deeply ingrained to suppress. We changed fashions, created new

markets, and muddied the difference between need and want only so that we could keep producing. We covered the planet with our production; we filled it to the very brim.

The Vienna Covenant of 2042 stated in no uncertain terms that no further structures could be erected. The planet had reached a saturation point, and if the species was to survive all inessential production would have to cease. This included all works of architecture. The protocol stipulated that works already under construction had until the end of the year to be completed, but nothing new was to be permitted.

The Park had just broken ground. A loophole in the legislature prohibited the erection of new unique structures on a single development site, but allowed the duplication of structures already existing. In the year that followed the Covenant the developers covered the site in a grid of hundreds of carousels.

For several years following completion the park was forgotten. However, as people began to venture out of their inert cities, starved for novelty that was no longer being built, the park was re-appropriated. Each identical carousel consisted of two arrays of seats rotating in opposite directions. People would come and sit and tell each other stories about spaces: spaces they had been to, spaces they had wished to see, and spaces that had never nor would ever exist.

The park was only a framework, a facilitator, of the stories. The gentle rotation of the carousels and the ever-changing pairings of narrator and

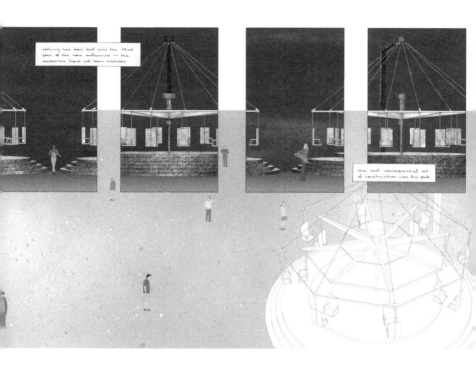

nothing has been built since the 42nd year of the new millennium — the resources have not been available

the last consequential act of construction was the park

the park was quickly appropriated by storytellers, starved for novelty that could no longer be built, operating in the last medium left to the mind.

each machine was the same:

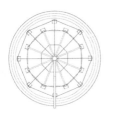

two concentric arrays of narrators

rotating in opposite directions

relating space to each other.

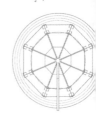

listener ensured that each participant experienced a different sequence of stories, and thus a different sequence of spaces – an exquisite corpse of a promenade, as unpredictable as the next narrator's imaginings working on the listener's interpretation.

An epic of spaces was thus collectively created within the boundaries of the minds in the park. They found an inexhaustible source of newness in this joint venture of the sharing of imagined space, a seemingly infinite sequences of probabilities. The spaces that evolved were not bounded by material limitations, client needs, or even gravity. They were constrained by language only, and they were the products of the pure exhilaration that accompanies creation.

Word of the park spread and more and more people flocked to the development from the surrounding cities, eager for a taste of new space. Every seat of every carousel was filled.

It was a simple and common occurrence to move between carousels. Narrators would bring with them common themes that had developed in their previous carousels, threads of ideas to be weaved into other stories. Spaces grew and diminished. Spaces evolved and acquired new appendages. The worst excesses of aestheticism were reached, and toppled because hundreds could inhabit the same building, and each would be in a different space.

For a time the people were satiated in this park of rearrangements and reconfigurations; however, imperceptibly at first, conditions began to change. Like water trickling out of a bathtub, the excitement waned. As the influx of newcomers dwindled, innovation weakened, though the craving

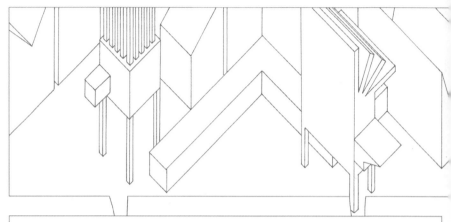

imagined spaces coalesced as each narrator experienced a different promenade composed of all the promenades previously evoked to him.

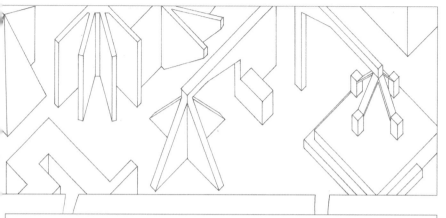

alas, over time, the spaces which had at first appeared so promisingly novel became painfully familiar as they realized all they had ever done was rearrange.

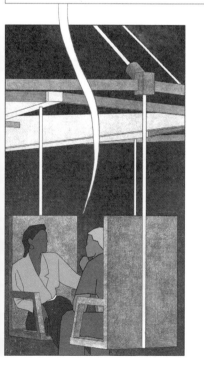

and appreciation for it remained strong. Stories devolved into repetition, and, it seemed, familiarity set in.

At first it was perceived simply as déjà vu, a barely noticed sensation of having experienced some element of the story before. Those that still had new stories to tell were revered. Instead of everyone sharing equally the tasks of narrator and listener those that still had new stories became the narrators, and those that had lost their stories became the listeners. But even these stories slipped into familiarity.

No one knew for how many months, or even years, the dullness had been growing. But grow it did, untraceably and incurably. The spaces narrated became increasingly recognizable, and still no one could pin down where from, or when. Again the distinction between narrators and listeners became blurred, as no one seemed to have any new spaces to tell. Unable to do anything else after so many years of storytelling, they persisted, even when every variation was lost – they were all telling the same space:

All that remained was the story of a grid of hundreds of carousels, gently rotating.

THE METAMORPHOSIS OF A GIRAFFE

By Hannah Cook

A long time ago –
And yet perhaps it wasn't such a
very long time ago –
There lived a city.
Where worn-out skyscrapers reminisced
of their gleaming heyday
And looked down upon factories, smoking away.
What once had glittered, stood veiled
by soot and smog;
Culture and energy now awash with a fog.
By the time of this tale, color had run dry;
All was leaden, except for the sky.
And one curious brute, down by the port;
A mighty crane, dignified and stalwart.
The huge beast heaved -
Containers as hefty as hephalumps -
From the vessels and ferries

Back breaking, joints wrenching
From dusk till dawn and dawn till dusk
For how long he had worked,
he could not remember.
It seemed he had begun a very long time ago –
When the sky was sun soaked blue
And seagulls had swooped around his ears –
And yet perhaps it wasn't such a
very long time ago?

It had started out as a cough and a splutter
The clouds were feeling a little off-color
But the malady worsened with smoke inhalation
Industry persisted in wreaking pollution
Congestion and choking gave way to black lung
And a darkness of spirit cast over the sun
In bleary sadness, the sky started to weep
Acid rain tears from rugged grey cheeks
Painted skin pealing the crane looked up
Shuddering clouds, "spare me, enough!"

Soon rain was bawling
Deluging, devouring
Banks of the basin
Broken in hours
The greatest of floods
Took to the streets
Reclaimed territories
Run amok, no retreat

The sky starting revolting
Bolting down pitch forks of lightning and roaring

And with waters uprising, in a last fulmination
A dazzling curse struck the crane

A metamorphosis! A transfiguration!
Crane to giraffe and elephant from container
A second of silence, not long enough for echo
Knee deep in water, stood two
brilliant incantations
Trembling legs, not used to terra firma
Born for barely a second, yet abided an era

Some time passed before the fierce storm waned
And living eyes dared to blink
And what a sight to see!
Glassy factories scoured by rising sea
Began to glimmer again

The elephant gleefully, gracelessly, snorkeled
Up street, down alleyway, round malls
Following triumphant trumpets
Wading through debris of cars and stalls
Cautiously, giraffe followed
"What hell had brewed up high?
In the cauldron of the sky
For her to descend such an
overwhelming quantity of things
Diabolical and terrifying sins?"
His head turned toward the horizon
And a glimpse of trees, birds and suns

The giraffe beckoned the elephant
"Come hither with me, beyond this flood, beyond

the sea"
They traveled together for day upon day
How long they walked for neither could say
But there they found paradise!
No smog and no smoke
Where both could breathe easy
And neither did choke

So the moral of this tale
If there is one to find
Is to keep in mind
The sorceress of the sky
Make her mad
And hubble bubble!
To poison her
Is powerful trouble

You've be forewarned,
So be aware
Of what you pump into the air.
She'll seek revenge for what you sew
It may just be the last thing you know!

THEE, LITTLE PIG

By Heidi Lee

Living in the brick house "happily ever after", the third little pig felt life was a little tedious after the big bad wolf became a pot of soup. One day while it was brushing its fur, a strand of hair got stuck to the brush. With a little pull to release it, a crisp sound of metal fell through and a small metal object tumbled out of the little pig's ear. Reaching to comfort that tiny ear the little pig startled at the strange object sitting on the ground.

"Where did you get this key?" asked mother pig who just came back from the back garden. The little pig told its mother what had just happened, so as she was folding the fresh clothes she murmured,

"But our story never had a key or a key hole. As I recall, the wolf has always just blew/climbed through the chimney. Anyway, fairy tales will never mention a pig entering a house using a key, that's far too close to reality."

"Reality?" The little pig mumbled.

"Mum, I want to leave the fairy tale and go into the real world, in search of the door that this key can open."

"...but the reality is nothing like where we are. It's cruel and dangerous!" Mother pig said worriedly.

She doesn't put much hope on the idea of "reality". However she can sense how the little pig has grown to believe that this key would open up a new road, something that is as wonderful as dreams or anticipations. Hugging onto this belief, the little pig crawled out of "The End" page under the reluctant eyes of its mother.

Having left the 2D world the first thing that it saw was a cityscape made up of different roofs of various heights. It raised its head all the way to the back of its neck to look at one of the pointy roofs reaching for the sky; it was like a pointy shoe and makes one wonder if something was hiding within the tip of it. As the little pig was daydreaming with its head held high, a voice came very close to its brain. It was the voice of a muscular tapir.

"Hi there, do you want to join us? Our factory is just the thing for you."

When the little pig heard that Mr. Tapir makes exterior walls, the little pig agreed to the work instantly.

"Perhaps instead of looking for that door, I can make one that belongs to this key!" it thought.

It was not long after the work started when the little pig has realized that Mr. Tapir was not after the abilities of the little pig but instead the nails grown on its trotters. They were perfect materials to make gelatin. The exterior walls that Mr. Tapir mentioned were in fact houses made from liquor-soaked biscuits, custard and jelly. Of course, these houses were made only from exterior walls. There was nothing but walls inside the house. The daily task of the little pig was nothing more than sitting next to the conveyor belt, clipping away the nails that Mr. Tapir asked for. Occasionally the

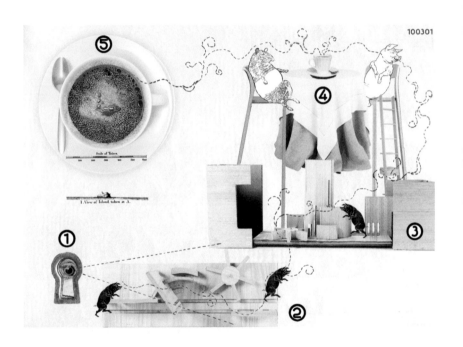

little pig might get sent to obtain molds from the pointy roof that it gazed at previously.

Inside this pointy roof stored a collection of beautiful jelly molds. Having taken out the mold with the correct number inside this magnificent archive, together with Mr. Tapir's recipe, the day's job would be smooth and swift. Mr. Tapir once said that this is the most aesthetic system that it has painstakingly devised, and there will never be any rooms for questioning. Of course, this includes all the doors and façade that the little pig tries to sneak in.

One night the little pig wanted to secretly sneak into that pointy roof to take a peek at the highest point. Through endless steps, the little pig eventually arrived at a tiny room on the top of the staircase. This room is in fact where the weathercock in duty lives. Sitting inside the room was a kinetic egg collector, and right in the center of the room a keyhole was floating in mid-air. The little pig excitingly searched for a step ladder and peeked through the hole eagerly.

Once the little pig's sight left the keyhole it was already inside it, wandering through the labyrinth of mechanical parts. Reaching towards the middle of the labyrinth, a round table with high legs was placed in the center where Mr. Tapir was already awaiting the arrival of the little pig. It signaled the little pig to climb onto the chair with the ladder, and when settled Mr. Tapir asked,

"Do you want to leave?" The little pig nodded.

"Then how about trading it for your lips?" The little pig nodded again. Placing the lip on the table, Mr Tapir showed a grin of satisfaction. It carefully placed a delicate bone china tea cup on the table and then slowly "it" said,

"Cross this sea"

The sea was spread with minuscule folds with an island in the center. Upon close inspection the island was tightly filled with ant-like people. The people on this island appear to move backward, living and traveling in reverse. Whilst the little pig could not take its eyes off this bizarre island the voice asked,

"Do you want to cross the sea?"

With a firm nod the little pig took the cup and drank quickly with the cup just about covering its face. Before the little pig was swollen by the cup the sound of a sign came from within. The little pig's sight returned to the edge of the cup and a different scene appeared.

It was foggy. There was nothing to be seen, apart from a thin 0.1mm line. The little pig picked up that line, pulled it a little, and recognized it as the front knot that extends to somewhere far ahead. It gazed onto the horizon for a moment, tied that line around its ears a few times and started to swirl towards the direction of the line. Its footstep seized when it reached a blob of blackness in front. The line has already formed a layer of hair on the top of the little pig's head.

Ahead of the little pig was indeed a village weaved together by hair, growing and constantly

transforming every second. Just like metabolism the houses made from hair cultivates and then sheds. At this rate of evolution, extra care was needed whilst walking in this village. The little pig held on to that strand of hair and entered into the village.

At the entrance was a person handing out a booklet, filled with information and rules about the village. Here at the hair village if you work repeatedly hard to develop the village without questioning you will receive its special produce: hair soy sauce. By selling this hair soy sauce gold coins can be obtained.

"If it's not possible to make a suitable door for the key, maybe I can buy one with the gold coins?" thought the little pig. With this belief it worked very hard to help build the village, from picking the best of hairs to separating them into different grades, washed and dried them carefully and then made wonderful forms from them. Obviously these cannot be achieved without special care.

One sunny afternoon the little pig was working hard trimming one of the skyscrapers when its stomach started to rumble. It must be tea time, yet the little pig was annoyingly reminded by the fact that it had forgotten to bring the teacake prepared earlier. Suddenly the little pig remembered its mother. Just before it left the fairy tale, mother pig gave the little pig a piece of bread hoping that one day it could be of use. The little pig tore apart the dense textures within the piece of bread with its teeth when a small circular box fell out. It had written "toad oil" on it.

This I have heard before thought the little pig. Once upon a time mother pig told the little pig that if applied as a thin layer to the face this "toad oil" does not only keep warmth, but more importantly can let one get a glimpse of "reality".

"But I am already in reality! Maybe I can put some on to keep me warm..." said the little pig. Secretly enjoying the thought of 'being in' reality, all of a sudden a drift of cocoa smell traveled through its nose together with the warmth on its face. The smell originated within the building that the little pig was trimming and through the window the little pig followed that wonderful smell. The inside wall of this building was filled with equal sized pigeon holes, and each one of them had a cuckoo bird working inside. Within the enormously high ceiling these birds flew around busily working on chocolates. This little pig watched how the molten chocolate fills the mold, gets cooled, packaged with foil and finally sprayed with a layer of gold paint. The birds collects these gold coins together, and as the little pig cautiously watched what was happening in front of him, it couldn't help but take out from its pocket the coin that it worked so hard to obtain. With a slight scratch at the edge a shiny 99% dark chocolate circle escaped from its sleeve. It was this moment that the hopes and plans of working hard to buy a door for the key became a transparent drift of vapor for the little pig.

Still staring at the happenings before its eyes, the little pig murmured.

"Is this Charlie and the Chocolate Factory?"

Isn't this more fairy tale than a fairy tale? What kind of reality is this? The little pig slowly turned its back, hoping that it can quietly escape this before too late, and then hopefully notify others. Yet...

"Arghhhhhh...................................."

When the little pig turned its back it accidentally fell into the conveyor belt of the chocolate coin manufacture, firstly squashed into shape, and then packaged in metal. Luckily, the key that was hiding inside the little pig's ear fell out during the squeeze and didn't make it inside the metal.

Next time when you use the key to open up this tin, maybe you can remember this fairy tale reality, and hopefully the little pig can provide you with enough calories to carry on searching for that door.

The End

RE:VOLVE

By Ivana Radmanovac & Iva Bekic

A priori Love,
The Earth revolves around the sun.
The Earth revolves once every twenty-four hours.

If you could spin, how long would you last?

At dawn, driven by the melody inside his flamboyant mind, He ran with lightness in his steps throughout the land like the wind, revolving everything he came across. All the living things, and the non living, gifting them life. It wanted to become bigger than itself. And it could.

"The world revolves around me. I am within myself. I would like to be more beautiful – if I could. But perfection hides the imperfections well. She on the other hand didn't see ME as the turning point".
(Concept, 100, sagittarius)
She likes to plan things. Likes to arrange them according to color. She was busy arranging flowers, scheming the candles and napkins. She has everything in her place as it ought to be. Everything that should, but not the one thing she would. The spin. The spin he could give her.
(Scheme, 28, virgo)

At noon, carried away by the melody inside his flamboyant mind, He ran with lightness in his steps throughout the land like the wind, revolving everything he came across. All the living things, and the non living, heavily making them heavenly. It wanted to become bigger than itself.

"You could be the prettiest of all, with colors that speak untold emotions. You could tell the truth about beauty. The beauty within and out of in. There would be no one with such live colorful skin

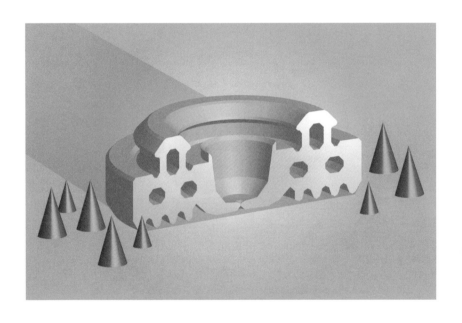

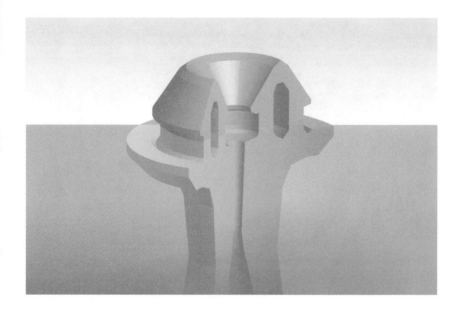

as you. As mesmerizing as a Queens dream could
be - You just have to spin!
For all that Earth cherishes, I could give you a
forest never touched before, wilderness in all its
purity from heaven itself. A forest that whispers
a melody of love. A palace made of wishes – You
just have to spin!
I could take you to the highest heights, where
the sky kisses the sea, and the sun touches the
sky. Who said sky is the limit, never believed he
could fly nor touch the sky. Spin!

Let me take you to a place I know you want to
go. Let me take you from nothing to everything,
where everything can be, where nothing is something, but no one cares about anything because
you have everything. From empty to full – you
have to spin!"

"Once I wanted to be the greatest, to be the
wildest dream, the highest height, or at least the
queen of the blue sky. All or nothing - It seemed
to be something. I started to spin and spinning
was fun, until one day it became a load of bun.
I can tell the truth about beauty, for beauty is in
me through others.
For all that Earth cherishes, a forest never touched
before is never alone. That is why it whispers a
melody of love. A palace made of wishes.
Highest heights, where the sky kisses the sea,
and the sun touches the sky: someone said sky is
the limit, because they believed they could touch
the sky, but the wind blows hard up there for you
to fly."

Revolve, revolve
made me dizzy,
so I was told.

At sunset, Concept ran throughout the land like
the wind revolving everything he came across. It
wanted to become bigger than itself. And it could.
@scheme If you could spin, how long would you
last?
@concept I'm not sure
@scheme don't you want to be everything?
@concept is being everything knowing about everything? Or knowing something about everything.
Everything about something. I tried getting my
head around it, but after a while, revolving around
myself had me seeing double. I wouldn't last a
whole 360. For you to be a whole, or more, you
need a hole.

The world revolves around him. He is within
himself. He would like to be more beautiful – if
he could. But perfection hides the imperfections
well. She on the other hand didn't see HIM as
the turning point. When there was nothing left,
he revolved the Earth itself. But then he could
not see anymore. He went blind. He was locked
inside. Waiting to be unlocked. The Earth revolves
around the sun. The Earth revolves once every
twenty-four hours.

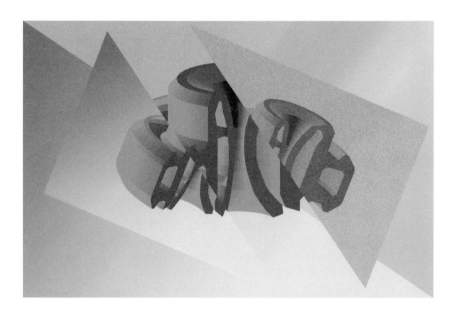

ANDY'S WINDOW

By JooYoung Ham & YooJin Lee

Mr. and Mrs. Archer decided to move to a new house. Andy went with his parents to the new house. The new house was a distance away from the town. Andy missed his friends, his old room, and things familiar to him. The move, the new house and loneliness made Andy sad. In the new house, Andy walked into his parents' room and stared at their window. Mr. and Mrs. Archer were discussing how to decorate their room. Andy wanted his parents to know how he was feeling.

"My room doesn't have a window," said Andy to his parents. Looking at the curtain in her room, Mrs. Archer said, "We need to get a new curtain for the room."

"I want to live in a room with a window," said Andy.

"Yes, we do need something." Mr. Archer said to his wife.

"What color of curtain should we get?" Mrs. Archer asked her husband.

No one was listening to Andy, so he walked back to his room. He was sad that his parents had ignored him. He did not like his room. It was just too dark.

The windowless room was so dark that it seemed flat. In his room Andy could feel the Darkness, but could not see it. Darkness was everywhere. In fact, it was all there was.

"My room is full of Darkness," said Andy to his parents.

"Yes, it is," Mr. Archer bluntly replied.

"Can I get a window in my room?" Andy pleaded to his parents.

"We will talk tomorrow; you need to go to bed now," Mrs. Archer told her son.

"But there is nothing good about my room," Andy mumbled to himself. He wanted his parents to care about how he felt.

Walking out from Andy's room Mrs. Archer said
to Andy, "I can't understand why you are being
so odd." It was clear to Andy that his parents did
not understand him. Andy and Darkness shared
the room together. There was no light in the room;
therefore, all Andy could see was Darkness. Andy
begged his parents to get him out of the Darkness. They did not see the problem, but Andy did.

"Where are you going?" Darkness called to
Andy.

"Who's there?" Andy answered, wondering
where the voice was coming from.

"I'm right here, can't you see me?" asked
Darkness.

Andy said, "I can't see at all," to which Darkness replied "There's no need to be afraid."

Andy felt something was pulling his leg.

"What is it?" Andy wondered back in his dark room.

"Where are you going?" Darkness asked, holding on to Andy's leg.

"I need to go and convince my parents about the window in my room." Andy mumbled to himself as he started walking again.

"You don't need a window." Darkness said as he swallowed Andy.

"Yes, I do. I want to see everything." Andy answered to Darkness.

Darkness changes Andy. Darkness is all around him. Andy learned that to associate with Darkness would not allow him to see others. Moreover, because he cannot Walking out from Andy's room Mrs. Archer said to Andy, "I can't understand why you are being so odd." It was clear to Andy

that his parents did not understand him. Andy and Darkness shared the room together. There was no light in the room; therefore, all Andy could see was Darkness. Andy begged his parents to get him out of the Darkness. They did not see the problem, but Andy did.

"Where are you going?" Darkness called to Andy.

"Who's there?" Andy answered, wondering where the voice was coming from.

"I'm right here, can't you see me?" asked Darkness.

Andy said, "I can't see at all," to which Darkness replied "There's no need to be afraid."

Andy felt something was pulling his leg.

"What is it?" Andy wondered back in his dark room.

"Where are you going?" Darkness asked, holding on to Andy's leg.

"I need to go and convince my parents about the window in my room." Andy mumbled to himself as he started walking again.

"You don't need a window." Darkness said as he swallowed Andy.

"Yes, I do. I want to see everything." Andy answered to Darkness.

Darkness changes Andy. Darkness is all around him. Andy learned that to associate with Darkness

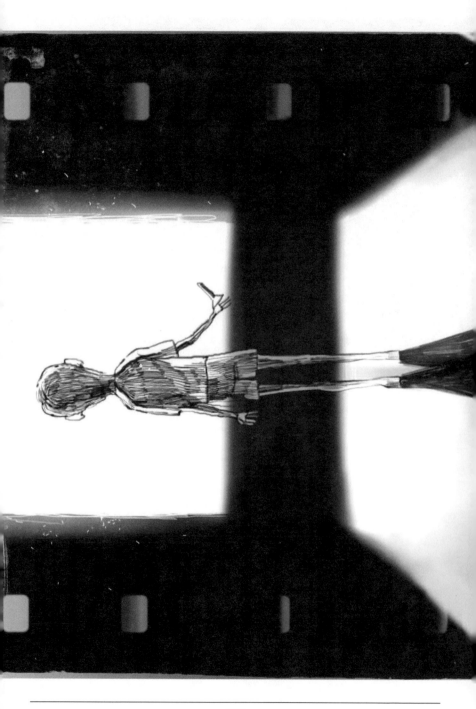

would not allow him to see others. Moreover,
because he cannot see, he cannot see himself and
his need for light grows stronger.

In the dim room, Andy sees an object flickering on the floor. It is a piece of chalk. The chalk
becomes a glimmer of hope for Andy to have a
window in his room. He reaches for a piece of
chalk and begins to sketch lines on the plain surface of the wall. The lines frame an opening. The
opening becomes a window on the concrete wall.
A sliver of light creeps into the room through the
new window.

By his own hand, Andy drew the light into his
space. The window becomes real and allows in
light. Andy is looking out the window and he is
mesmerized by what this light is doing. As his
eyes get accustomed to the light, he starts to see
more forms. He looks around, but he does not see
Darkness anymore.

"Where are you?" Andy said as he was looking
for Darkness.

"I'm right here." Darkness replies from the
back.

Andy turns around and sees his own shadow
and smiles. The light allows Darkness to become
Andy's shadow. Andy finally gets to see Darkness because he found light. Light defines forms
in Darkness. Darkness was no longer opaque,
but translucent. They both look out the window.
Andy looks out the window as the light he drew is
drawn into the space. He is satisfied that he has
solved the problem of Darkness with light. He has
given form to Darkness and given way to light.

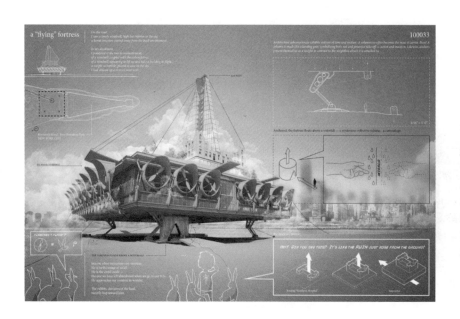

A "FLYING" FORTRESS

By Artur Dabrowski

On the road,
I saw a lonely windmill,
high but inferior to the sky.
A banal structure ousted away from the built
environment.

In my daydream,
I pondered of the two in reconcilement;
of a windmill coupled with the urban fabric,
of a windmill appearing to lift up and take
a building in flight...
a weight so terrible placed at ease in the sky.
I had dreamt up a flying fortress.

Below, a boy encounters my creation.
He is in the image of us all.
He is the child inside —
the one we have left abandoned when we go to our
9-5s.
He approaches my creation in wonder.

Atop this wind-turbine-powered machine sits a
ruin displaced from the site below. The rabbits,
denizens of the land, merrily hop toward him and

exclaim: "Hey! Did you see this? It's like the ruin
just rose from the ground!" The child is too shy
to reply. He simply follows the rabbits toward the
entrance shrouded by a waterfall — a mysterious
reflective volume. Behind the waterfall is a mirrored surface, reflecting the site... a camouflage.

Inside the waterfall

But a building cannot fly. This, I know.

I cannot preach blasphemy,
for that goes against the oath of my trade.
This craft is merely the magic of architecture.
Like a nest, the building is perched.
It sits on thin spider legs and a waterfall
— a black threshold.

Inside this void,
the noble inheritors of space are
transported from one unfamiliar
context to another.
They become foreigners
traveling through space.

The threshold does serve other purposes
than to conceal a massive structure.
The most eccentric is its digital display;
a feeling comparable to stepping inside
the notification center of an iDevice.

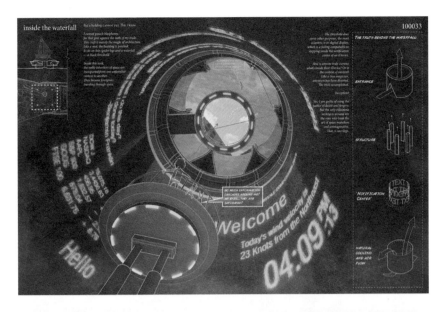

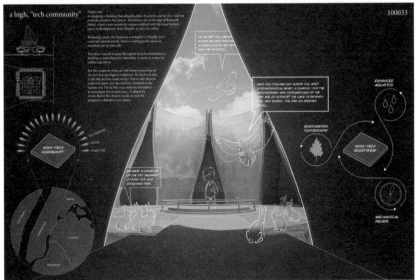

Inside this cylindrical space, the waterfall cascades 360°.
And in the center, a hydraulic platform lifts upward.
LED lights glow behind the water, flashing the date, the
weather, any and all types of data. The naive rabbits, enlightened: "so much information cascades around me!"

And is anyone truly curious
what's inside their iDevice? Or is the content of interest?
Like a true magician,
attention has been diverted.
The trick accomplished.

Deception?

Well, yes. I am guilty of using
the tactics of deceit and forgery.
But the only villainous architects around
are the ones who treat the art
of space mundane and unimaginative.
That, is sacrilege.

A high, "tech comunity"

Forgive me,
in designing a building that allegedly
defies its gravity and its site,
I did not properly introduce the context.
The fortress sits at the edge of Roosevelt Island,
where a new university campus outfitted
with the latest technology is in development.
Solar lilypads, as they are called.

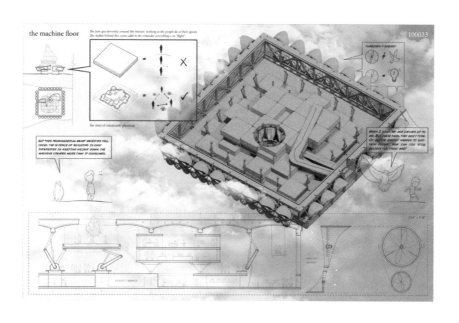

Technology aside,
the lilypad as a metaphor is blandly
just a corporate advertisement.
There is nothing poetic
about its mundane use of solar cells.

Therefore I saw fit to grant
the highest of tech communities
a building so technologically impossible,
to serve as a muse of endless aspiration.

But the creatures of the air will always remind us
that our flight is restricted. No bird is at rest in the
sky, so how could we be? That is why there is a
discreet mesh over the turbines, invisible to the
human eye. Try as they may, birds are forbidden
to investigate... to dispel the secret. But to the
child in us all, we may be tempted to disbelieve
our senses.

When the elevator stops, an owl swoops from
the sky: "ah haha! You cannot see what's above
this waterfall; a land unlike any other... ooh the
mystery." Although the boy is bewildered, his
company is excited to meet a creature of the sky
halfway! A first for their grounded feet! Circling,
the owl continues: "have you figured out where
you are? A technological beast; a complex for the
businessmen and intellectuals of the new age of
science! The land is beneath you, and surely,
you are on another level..."

The machine floor

The fans spin fervently around the interior, working
as the people do at their computers.
The skyline behind their desks adds to the reminder
that everything is in "flight".

"But this technological beast deceives you, child.
The science of building is only interested in keeping
weight down. The machine creates more than it
consumes." The wise owl rants. "These turbines are
not wings like mine. When I soar, my age catches up
to me. But these fans, they don't tire. In fact, they
become more energetic with every cycle. Of all the
energy needed to sustain flight, how can you still
believe you truly are?"

Skyward

Ah but the illusion of flight isn't just an optical illusion.
To an observer: the building flies.
To an occupant: the ground disappears, and they are
in flight.
To a person above: they themselves, are soaring.

The boy ventures away and emerges onto a natural
topography, engineered on the roof. The rabbits run,
unable to contain their excitement. But the boy is
saddened, disappointed in the reality of this 'fortress'. A rabbit comes to him: "how can the truth

bring you down when you're up so high? Isn't this
the most wondrous of views? A paradise! The
wind is in the air, the vibrations are in our soles,
we are in flight!"

Outside, there is no denying the senses.
The ground sways below,
as the clouds are at reach.
The poeticism is not that an object can fly
but once there, a person feels in flight.
Space becomes us.
We produce in factories,
we lounge in lounges,
we fly in flying apparatuses.

The child inside will always remain
to enjoy the wonder of space.

Above, an educated man stands at the edge of my
creation. The windmills spin. The water crashes.
He is aware of what powers his monitor and what
holds up his chair. Yet he says to himself:

"If nature must become artificial... let it be magical
like this. Why imitate when we can fulfill nature's
impossible dreams?"

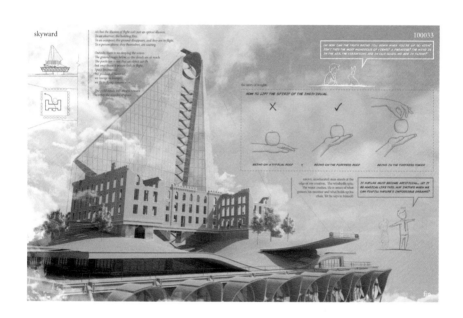

ACKNOWLEDGMENTS

Our heartfelt thanks go to all of the individuals and companies that have supported us throughout the Fairy Tales competition.

Thank you to our wonderful jury: Will Alsop, Paula Scher, Mitchell Joachim, Jack Zipes, Nigel Coates, Francesco Lipari, and the ever-mysterious Klaus. Their considerable input and support helped us to reach new heights.

A special thank you to all of our media partners, and the amazing teams behind them: Design-Milk, Europaconcorsi, Cityvision, KNSTRCT, Archilovers, Archiportale, e-architect, archi-ninja, Arco web, Arquimaster, Metalocus and Arch Student each helped us to spread our message far and wide.

An additional thank you to the two talented designers behind this book: Vicente Garcia Morillo who is responsible for the Blank Space identity and also the cover of this book; and Claire Eckstrom who had the considerable task of designing the interior of this book.

Most importantly, a huge thank you to the over 300 teams who entered the competition from around the world. The tenacity and imagination that each entrant infused into their entry was far beyond our wildest dreams, and it helped to fulfill our purpose of uncovering better means to communicate architecture, and in turn, to change the way that the world perceives architecture. The response to the competition is a testament to the power of these ideas.

ABOUT BLANK SPACE

Blank Space is an online platform for architecture, founded in 2013 by Matthew Hoffman and Francesca Giuliani-Hoffman. Matthew is an architect who believes architecture can be more interesting, more fun and more social. Francesca is a journalist who believes that communication is omnipresent, and that good communication helps great ideas change the world.

We like to think of Blank Space as an office for thought provocation, challenging architecture to rethink its role in society by speaking about things everybody can relate to, in a language understandable to all. Every endeavor that we initiate takes fun very seriously and strives to be audacious enough to ignite imaginations.

Through competitions, publications, and projects, we uncover the true power of architecture by creating new opportunities for design to engage the public.